QUANTUM THEORY
A CRASH COURSE

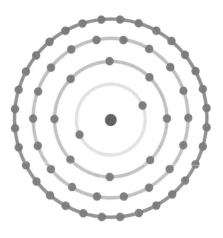

QUANTUM THEORY
A CRASH COURSE

BECOME AN INSTANT EXPERT!

Brian Clegg

METRO BOOKS
New York

METRO BOOKS
New York

An Imprint of Sterling Publishing
1166 Avenue of the Americas
New York, NY 10036

ISBN: 978-1-4351-6970-8

For information about custom editions, special sales,
and premium and corporate purchases, please contact
Sterling Special Sales at 800-805-5489
or specialsales@sterlingpublishing.com.

Manufactured in China

1 3 5 7 9 10 8 6 4 2

www.sterlingpublishing.com

Credits: *Art Director* James Lawrence;
Design JC Lanaway;
Illustrators Nick Rowland, Andrea Ucini;
Series concept design Michael Whitehead

INTRODUCTION

Quantum physics is often regarded as obscure and weird. While it can certainly be counterintuitive, the reputation for obscurity is misplaced. Quantum theory explains the interactions of electrons, subatomic particles, and photons of light. As such, it provides a key foundation of our understanding of the world in general. Nearly everything we interact with is composed of these quantum particles. Whether we are thinking of matter, light, or phenomena such as electricity and magnetism, these tiny components are at work.

It might seem that we never experience quantum objects as separate entities, but quantum phenomena have a huge impact on our lives. It has been estimated that thirty-five percent of GDP in developed countries involves technology—notably electronics, but also materials science, medicine, and more—that could not be constructed without a knowledge of the theory behind the amazing quantum.

Probability to the fore

So, where does the apparent strangeness come from? That word "quantum" refers to something that comes in chunks rather than being continuous. And the result of applying this chunky approach to the natural world proved a shock to its discoverers. It turned out that quantum entities are very different from the objects that we can see and touch. Quantum particles do not behave like tiny tennis balls. Instead, left to their own devices, quantum particles cease to have distinct properties such as location and direction of spin. Instead, they exist solely as an array of probabilities until they interact with something else. Before that interaction takes place, all we can say about a quantum particle is that it has a certain probability of being here, another probability of being there, and so on.

This is very different from the familiar probability of the toss of a coin. When we toss a fair coin, there is a 50/50 chance of it being heads or tails. Fifty percent of the time that we look at the tossed coin, it will be heads, and fifty percent of the time, it will be tails. However, in reality, once the coin has been tossed, it has a specific value with one hundred percent certainty—we just do not know what that value is until we look. But in quantum theory, all that exists until we take a look at the quantum equivalent of a coin is the probabilities.

It is easy to regard quantum particles as strange. But we need to bear in mind that this is what nature is like. The only reason we think of such behavior as weird is that we are used to the way large-scale objects work—and, in a sense, it is their behavior that is odd, because they do not seem like the ordinary quantum particles that make them up. The biggest struggle that quantum physicists have had over the years has not been with the science, but with finding an interpretation of what is happening that could form a bridge between everyday observations and events at the quantum level. Even today, there is no consensus among physicists on how quantum theory should be interpreted. Many simply accept that the math works well and get on with it, a philosophy known as "shut up and calculate."

The quantum revolution

This lack of fixed values for properties of particles did not sit comfortably for some of the earliest scientists involved in quantum theory at the beginning of the twentieth century. Notably, both Max Planck, who came up with the basic concept that light could be quantized, and Albert Einstein, who showed that this quantization was real and not just a useful calculating tool, hated the intrusion of probability into what they felt should be the fixed and measurable reality of nature. Einstein was convinced for his entire career that beneath the apparent randomness and probability there was some structure, something that behaved like the "ordinary" physical world. Yet all the evidence is that he was wrong.

The younger players, starting with Niels Bohr, and people such as Erwin Schrödinger, Werner Heisenberg, Paul Dirac, and Max Born, quantified probability-driven quantum behavior during the 1920s. Their progress was remarkable. These were theoreticians who had little time for experiment. Their ideas could be described as inspired guesswork. And yet the mathematics they developed matched what was later observed in experiments with impressive accuracy.

From the 1930s to the present day, there were a whole string of technological advancements in electronics, the development of the laser, the increasing employment of superconductivity, and more, each of which made direct use of the supposedly weird behavior of quantum particles. It is hard to deny something exists when you build it into gadgets found in every home. And the trigger for quantum physics to move from obscurity to center stage would be World War II.

Many of the key players in the second and third generation of quantum physicists, from Niels Bohr to Richard Feynman, played a significant role in World War II. Their involvement primarily revolved around nuclear fission. In 1938, German physicist Otto Hahn and Austrian physicist Lise Meitner demonstrated radioactive decay, a quantum process, subject to the same influence of probability as other behaviors of quantum particles. In itself, nuclear fission was interesting, but the importance of the process became clear when combined with the idea of the chain reaction. It could either run as a controlled reaction, generating heat, or given its head, it could run away with itself in an ever-increasing cascade, producing a nuclear explosion.

As the world headed unsteadily toward all-out war, there was a fear that Germany—with Denmark and Austria key centers for quantum physics—would produce a nuclear weapon, giving it a terrifying military advantage. In response to this threat, one of the first of the familiar names in the quantum theory story to become involved was Albert Einstein. Einstein was a lifelong pacifist, and it had not occurred to him that the intersection of $E = mc^2$ and nuclear decay could produce a devastating bomb. He was asked to sign letters to the US authorities—and President Roosevelt was persuaded into action, setting up the Manhattan Project, which saw the United States produce and deploy the first atomic bombs in 1945.

Quantum becomes practical

Many key quantum physicists left continental Europe, either because they had a Jewish background or were horrified by the rise of the Nazis. Schrödinger went to Ireland and Born to Scotland. Meitner, who had moved to Stockholm, was invited to join the Manhattan Project, but wanted nothing to do with the bomb. Meanwhile, a young Feynman was drafted into the project. Bohr helped refugee scientists from Germany find new academic homes. He remained in occupied Denmark, but refused to be involved with the German nuclear program. It was in Copenhagen that he was visited by the most controversial of his colleagues, Heisenberg, who led the German project. Exactly what happened in the meeting has never been clear—but it seems likely that Heisenberg hoped to get help from Bohr. Bohr escaped to Sweden in 1943 when it seemed likely he would be arrested. He was a regular presence at Los Alamos where the US bomb was developed, providing consultancy.

In the end, Heisenberg failed—whether, as he later claimed, because he did not want to produce a weapon, or because it was simply too difficult. The vast Manhattan Project succeeded, and quantum physics changed the world. Wartime also saw electronics start to take off as early electronic computers were constructed to help with the war effort. The Colossus development at Bletchley Park in the UK went into full operation in 1944 cracking German ciphers, while in the United States, the more sophisticated ENIAC was running by 1946, making calculations for hydrogen bomb development.

These early computers used traditional vacuum tubes, which were fragile, bulky, and needed a lot of energy to run. They were the last leading-edge development to depend on electronics where an appreciation of quantum theory was not essential. It is no surprise that quantum physics was brought to the fore just one year after ENIAC went live with the development of the first working transistor. The wartime developments showed the potential for electronics to transform the world, but it took quantum devices to make electronic devices feasible mass-market products.

A quantum journey

To explore the development of quantum science, and applications from lasers and transistors through superconducting magnets and quantum computers, we will divide the subject into four sections, pulling together fifty-two bite-size articles with features covering key aspects and characters in the development of our quantum understanding of the world.

The first chapter, **Foundations**, brings in Planck's initial (and in his words, desperate) invocation of the quantum to explain an odd behavior of hot, glowing objects. We will see how Einstein showed the concept was real, and how the way different atoms give off and absorb a range of colors of light is central to Bohr's model of a quantum atom. Here, electrons cannot occupy any orbit, like planets around a star, but rather can exist only in fixed shells, jumping between them in quantum leaps.

We will discover how quantum physics blurs the concepts of a wave and a particle and how the mathematical developments to explain quantum behavior brought probability into our understanding, leading to the taunting thought experiment that is Schrödinger's cat. We will see how Heisenberg's uncertainty principle and Pauli's exclusion principle made it clear that we could never know everything about quantum systems, and how these quantum principles shape the reactions of chemical elements. And we will find out how quantum physics brought in a new property of quantum particles called spin—which has nothing to do with rotating.

In the second chapter, **Quantum Behavior**, we discover the implications for the involvement of probability and how physicists attempted to reconcile the probabilistic nature of particles with the apparently ordinary behavior of the objects made up of them. We will see how the concepts of fields and infinite seas of negative-energy electrons transformed the mathematical representation of the quantum, and how all the interactions of matter and light came under the quantum banner. We will

explore strange quantum concepts such as zero-point energy, quantum tunneling, and experiments where particles appear to travel faster than light.

For the third chapter, **Interpretation & Entanglement**, we move onto two of the strangest aspects of quantum science. We discover why, uniquely in physics, quantum theory has a wide range of interpretations (even though the mathematical outcomes remain the same, whichever interpretation is used). And, with quantum entanglement, we uncover Einstein's greatest challenge to quantum theory. He was the first to show that the strange quantum effect of entanglement implies that a measurement on one of a pair of specially linked quantum particles will be instantly reflected in the other particle, even if it is on the opposite side of the universe. Einstein felt that quantum entanglement proved that quantum theory was irreparably flawed, as this "spooky action at a distance" seemed impossible. But experiments have shown that entanglement exists and can be used both for unbreakable encryption and to transfer quantum properties from one particle to another.

The final chapter, **The Amazing Quantum**, concentrates on a mix of applications and special quantum states of matter. We discover the purely quantum origins of the laser, transistor, electron microscope, and MRI scanner. These last require superconductivity, a quantum phenomenon that is still not wholly understood. Elsewhere, we see other quantum oddities such as superfluids, which, once started, carry on moving indefinitely and can climb out of a vessel on their own. And we find out why quantum effects turn up in biology, before considering the ultimate quantum challenge. Can quantum physics ever be made compatible with Einstein's general theory of relativity and its explanation of gravity?

Strange—but real

Quantum physics may be strange—but that does not make it incomprehensible, just amazing and wonderful. This is, after all, the science that describes the behavior of the atoms that make you and everything around you—not to mention the light that enables you to see and carries the energy from the Sun that makes life on Earth possible. Oh, and without which we would have no phones or televisions or computers or internet. So, what better subject for a crash course?

How to use this book

This book distills the current body of knowledge into 52 manageable chunks, allowing you to choose whether to skim-read or delve in a bit deeper. There are four chapters, each containing 13 topics, prefaced by a set of biographies of the leading quantum physicists. The introduction to each chapter gives an overview of some of the key events you might need to navigate.

The Drill-Down looks at one element of the main concept in more detail, to give another angle or to enhance understanding.

Each topic has three paragraphs.

The Main Concept provides an overview of the theory.

QUANTUM SPIN

Matter is a short, memorable fact.

"A theoretical interpretation had to be found at any price . . . I was prepared to sacrifice any of my previous physics convictions."

MAX PLANCK
LETTER OF PLANCK TO R. W. WOOD OCTOBER 7, 1931

1
FOUNDATIONS

THE DEATH OF VICTORIAN PHYSICS

By 1900, physics was a solidly Victorian affair. The foundations of physics came from the work of Galileo and Newton, which underwent small tweaks in the years that followed. However, the nineteenth century saw an explosion of developments that both expanded the discipline's reach and took earlier ideas to dizzy new heights.

The importance of the steam engine to the industrial revolution meant that the science of thermodynamics came to the fore. Equally, electricity and magnetism, began to be understood in ways that enabled them to be put to practical use. The work of Scottish physicist James Clerk Maxwell brought light into the fold as an electromagnetic wave.

Two clouds

It is often said that by 1900 there was a smugness among physicists, who felt that only fine details remained to be sorted out. Specifically, the other great nineteenth-century Scottish physicist, William Thomson, also known as Lord Kelvin, is frequently quoted as saying "There is nothing new to be discovered in physics now. All that remains is more and more precise measurement." There is no evidence that Kelvin ever said this, however. Perhaps the closest we have to the assertion came from Max Planck's professor, Philipp von Jolly, when he suggested Planck study the piano rather than science as there was little left to do.

What Kelvin did say was that there were two clouds obscuring key aspects of physics. The first was the wave nature of light, which it was assumed required a medium, called the ether, in which the light could wave. But no experiment detected the ether's presence. And the second cloud Kelvin called the "Maxwell–Boltzmann doctrine regarding the partition of energy." This resulted in a phenomenon that became known as the "ultraviolet catastrophe."

Between them, Kelvin's clouds were the precursors of changes that transformed physics in the twentieth century. The first resulted in Einstein's special theory of relativity, making Newton's laws of motion a special case for relatively low speeds. The special theory itself then inspired Einstein's general theory, transforming our understanding of gravity. Similarly, finding a solution to the second cloud resulted in the first move toward the development of quantum physics.

These twin giants—relativity and quantum theory—became the foundations of physics; practically all other aspects of the subject became influenced by them or subsumed into them. The reason, perhaps, that this transformation is not widely understood is that schools still teach a primarily Victorian physics curriculum. Although there is often an advantage in teaching subjects through historical processes, when there is such a significant transformation, it is very strange to ignore it. It seems likely that Victorian physics is preserved because relativity and quantum theory are considered "difficult."

When we look at the period when Victorian physics was being displaced, it is not surprising that there was resistance at the time. Max Planck and Albert Einstein, both significant contributors to the origins of quantum physics, each had issues with it. Yet the successful idea that Planck used to fix the ultraviolet catastrophe and Einstein employed in an explanation of the photoelectric effect tore a hole in the understanding of the nature of light. It required light to be quantized—broken up into chunks or packets, rather than progressing as a continuous wave.

The cost of the quantum

Quantization itself was not an issue—it's a common enough concept. For example, cash is quantized. There is no 0.513-cent coin. Physical currency has a quantum of 1 cent, and there is nothing smaller. Similarly, atoms quantized matter. The whole idea of an atom at the start of the twentieth century (which admittedly was incorrect) was that it was indivisible. The word "atom" comes from the Greek for "uncuttable." So why did quantizing light produce a revolution in physics?

Initially, it was because of the move away from light being purely considered as a wave. But the aspects of quantum physics that disturbed Einstein—the introduction of probability as a fundamental aspect of nature, and the way that quantum physics made the act of measurement itself more significant than some underlying reality—were more likely causes for longer-term resistance. However, by the 1930s, only a few clung onto the past. All aspects of quantum theory may not be known or fully understood, but there is no doubt that physics itself was totally transformed by the work of the quantum physicists.

BIOGRAPHIES

MAX PLANCK (1858–1947)

Compared with the young radicals of quantum physics, Max Planck came from an older, stiffer generation. Born in Göttingen, Germany, in 1858, he remained solidly Victorian in his approach. When Planck was preparing for university, he could equally have chosen music or physics, as he excelled at both and was a concert-class pianist. Physics won out, though, and Planck was particularly drawn to the topics of heat and energy. From this came his attempt on the ultraviolet catastrophe.

Planck solved this mysterious behavior of matter by taking what he later described as a lucky guess, treating electromagnetic radiation as if it came in the form of packets of energy rather than continuous waves. This proved a great success, although Planck would never accept that it was anything more than a useful mathematical work-around. Although he won the Nobel Prize in 1918 for this work, he was never comfortable with quantum physics.

In later life, Planck was dogged by personal tragedy. The eldest of his three sons was killed in World War I, both his daughters died in childbirth, and his youngest son was caught up in a plot to assassinate Hitler and executed. Planck died two years later in 1947 at the age of eighty-nine.

NIELS BOHR (1885–1962)

Born in 1885 in Copenhagen, Niels Bohr was a central figure in the development of quantum physics. Shortly after gaining his doctorate, he headed to England to spend a year working with J. J. Thomson at Cambridge. Bohr and Thomson did not hit it off, but Bohr received an invitation to move to Ernest Rutherford's lab in Manchester, England. Here, he was able to build on Rutherford's work on the structure of the atom to publish a quantum model of the hydrogen atom in 1913.

Some found Bohr difficult to communicate with. However, he became the hub of the development of quantum physics. He was also a regular sparring partner for Einstein, who disliked the probabilistic nature of quantum theory and regularly challenged Bohr with thought experiments.

Heading up the Institute of Theoretical Physics in Copenhagen from 1921, Bohr was awarded the Nobel Prize in 1922 and made valuable progress on the liquid drop model of the atomic nucleus, which proved essential for the development of nuclear fission. In 1943, he left Nazi-occupied Denmark. He returned to his beloved Copenhagen in 1945, from where he was involved in establishing the CERN laboratory. Bohr died in 1962, aged seventy-seven.

ERWIN SCHRÖDINGER (1887–1961)

Born in 1887 in Vienna, Erwin Schrödinger won his doctorate in 1910 and served as an artillery officer during World War I. By the 1920s, he had become professor of theoretical physics at Zurich. Here, he developed his own take on the emerging quantum theory with a wave-based approach that led to the formulation of his famous equation.

Although he got on well with Niels Bohr, Schrödinger disliked the concept of superposition of states that was central to Bohr's approach and devised the "Schrödinger's cat" thought experiment to underline its absurdity.

Schrödinger left Austria in 1933 (when he was awarded the Nobel Prize); on his return in 1936, he found that his absence was considered an "unfriendly act" by the Nazi regime and in 1938 had to leave hurriedly for Ireland, where he was appointed director of the Institute for Advanced Studies in Dublin. He remained there seventeen years, writing the influential book *What is Life?* describing the relationship between physics and living organisms.

Schrödinger's family life was complex. Although he remained married to Anny for forty years until his death in Vienna in 1961, aged seventy-three, he had a number of mistresses, and all his children were born to other women.

WERNER HEISENBERG (1901–1976)

Born in Würzberg, Germany, in 1901, Werner Heisenberg was a promising young physicist who became immersed in the developing field of quantum mechanics, producing his own highly mathematical approach to describing the behavior of quantum systems when he was only twenty-five. He went on to make significant contributions to the field until the 1930s, winning the Nobel Prize in 1932.

Initially, the Nazi regime treated Heisenberg with suspicion as he taught "Jewish physics" and was sometimes referred to as a "white Jew." However, the head of the SS, Heinrich Himmler, seemed to be persuaded of his value, and from 1938, Heisenberg was treated far better. He remained in Germany throughout the war, working on nuclear fission, traveling to occupied Copenhagen to meet Niels Bohr. Although he later claimed that he made every effort to slow down the German development of nuclear weapons, the degree of his resistance is unclear.

After the war, Heisenberg was a leading figure in German physics, heading up the Kaiser Wilhelm Institute for Physics, which was soon renamed the Max Planck Institute. Heisenberg died in 1976, at the age of seventy-four.

TIMELINE

PHOTONS
To explain the photoelectric effect, Albert Einstein makes the radical assumption that Planck's quanta of light, later known as photons, are real. Planck had used them as a convenience for calculations, but Einstein considered them actual physical entities. This work would win Einstein the Nobel Prize.

1900

1905

1913

QUANTA
Max Planck suggests that to get around the problems of the ultraviolet catastrophe, it should be assumed that electromagnetic radiation, including visible light, is given off as tiny packets of energy, known as quanta, with the energy depending on the frequency of the light and a constant.

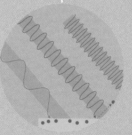

QUANTUM LEAP
Niels Bohr produces a quantum model of the hydrogen atom. This explains why an atom's electrons don't spiral into the nucleus, by using only fixed orbits to jump between, undertaking quantum leaps. It also explains why different elements give off and absorb specific frequencies of light.

MATRIX MECHANICS

Werner Heisenberg develops a more comprehensive mathematical description of the behavior of quantum particles called matrix mechanics. This puzzled many physicists as it had no analogies to familiar structures such as waves, but instead depended solely on arrays of numbers.

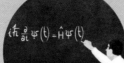

THE UNCERTAINTY PRINCIPLE

Heisenberg adds to his work with his uncertainty principle, which involves linked pairs of properties of quantum particles, such as momentum and position in space, or energy and position in time. The uncertainty principle says that the more accurately we know one of these properties, the less we can know about the other.

1925　　**1926**　　**1927**

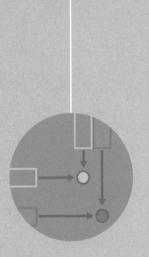

PROBABILITIES

Erwin Schrödinger publishes his own approach to the behavior of quantum particles, in the form of a wave equation, which describes the probability of finding a particle at any location, and how those probabilities evolve over time. Paul Dirac would later show that Heisenberg's and Schrödinger's approaches were exactly equivalent.

A SMALL PROBLEM

THE MAIN CONCEPT | At the end of the nineteenth century, there was a feeling of satisfaction in physics. A remarkable amount of the observed behavior of matter had been explained, and only a handful of issues remained. One of these became known as the ultraviolet catastrophe. This was a problem of black-body radiation. The radiation was the electromagnetic waves given off by all matter, whether visible light—such as the glow of a heated piece of metal—or invisible infrared or ultraviolet. A black body here is a hypothetical perfect absorber of radiation, which made for easier calculations and was a good approximation to real matter. The physical theory of the time made a very accurate prediction of how this radiation was actually produced when it came to low-frequency waves. But it also seemed to show that the higher the frequency was, the more of that radiation should be given off—which meant that everything, even at room temperature, should be blasting out large quantities of ultraviolet. In 1900, Max Planck spotted a fix that turned the prediction into a good match for all frequencies of light. But he had to assume that electromagnetic radiation—including visible light—didn't come in waves, but in tiny packets, which he called quanta.

DRILL-DOWN | Black bodies are theoretical constructs that provide a way of simplifying some of the realities of objects we see around us to make them relatively easy to describe using mathematics. A black body absorbs all incoming electromagnetic radiation, whereas a real object, for example a piece of metal, usually reflects some light, giving the object color. A black body does emit some electromagnetic radiation, but the frequency of that radiation is solely dependent on the body's temperature. At room temperature, only invisible infrared black-body radiation is produced. As an object is heated more, it starts to give off visible black-body radiation, glowing with heat.

MATTER | *Max Planck was an accomplished musician; in 1874, he spoke to physics professor Phillip von Jolly to help decide between a music or physics degree. Von Jolly recommended music as, aside from minor matters such as the ultraviolet crisis, there was little original left to do in physics. Planck decided he could live with this and would be happy refining details.*

QUANTA
Page 22
THE PHOTOELECTRIC EFFECT
Page 24
WAVE/PARTICLE DUALITY
Page 30

QUANTA

THE MAIN CONCEPT | Although the word "quanta" is not necessarily familiar, it's the plural of the more recognizable "quantum." It just means an amount of something (hence the James Bond movie *Quantum of Solace*)—but by introducing quanta, Max Planck unwittingly started a revolution in the way the physics of matter and light was treated. Planck was uncomfortable with his new approach, in part because it seemed like a painful backward step. In the early seventeenth century, Isaac Newton thought that light consisted of tiny particles he called "corpuscles," but many of Newton's contemporaries thought light was a wave. Since the early 1800s, this had been clearly established both experimentally and theoretically when Scottish physicist James Clerk Maxwell showed that light was an electromagnetic wave, a traveling interaction between electricity and magnetism. However, English physicists Lord Rayleigh and James Jeans had since shown that treating light as a continuous wave produced the ultraviolet catastrophe, where anything at room temperature should pour out ultraviolet light. By dividing a beam of light into tiny packets of energy—quanta, which he originally called "energy elements"—Planck produced a theory that for the first time matched what was actually observed. Planck saw his quanta simply as a convenient way to make theory fit reality but did not believe that electromagnetic radiation really consisted of these particles.

DRILL-DOWN | Each quantum of electromagnetic radiation has a very specific value: the energy of such a light quantum is the frequency of the radiation multiplied by a new constant of nature that we now call Planck's constant, represented by h. Planck's constant is tiny, just 6.626×10^{-34} joules per second. Compare this with the energy consumed by a 5-watt lightbulb, which is around 10 billion trillion trillion times larger. Traditionally, the color of light was linked to its wavelength, but Planck's constant shows that color is also a measure of the energy of light quanta. The snappier term "photons" replaced "light quanta" after it was coined by US chemist Gilbert Lewis.

MATTER | *James Clerk Maxwell developed a model that predicted a wave of electricity could produce a wave of magnetism, producing a wave of electricity, forming a self-sustaining electromagnetic wave. His model predicted a speed for this wave that he thought was close to the speed of light, but he had to wait until he returned to London from his summer break in rural Scotland to confirm it.*

A SMALL PROBLEM
Page 20

THE PHOTOELECTRIC EFFECT
Page 24

WAVE/PARTICLE DUALITY
Page 30

THE PHOTOELECTRIC EFFECT

THE MAIN CONCEPT | In 1902, Hungarian–German physicist Philipp Lenard discovered that shining ultraviolet light on metals in a vacuum produced "cathode rays"—which had recently been identified as streams of electrons. The energy in the light was producing electricity. Of itself, it wasn't surprising that, with sufficient energy, light would be able to knock electrons free. But this photoelectric effect did not behave as it should. If light were a wave—as had been thought since the nineteenth century—then the more intense the light, the more electrons would be produced. This is the equivalent of big waves doing more damage on a beach. However, Lenard discovered that light of only relatively short wavelengths would produce any electrons. Red light, for example, which has a longer wavelength than ultraviolet, produced no electrons, however intense the light. This was still a mystery in 1905 when the young Albert Einstein, working in the Swiss Patent Office, used Planck's quanta to explain the photoelectric effect. He said that, if quanta were real rather than just a useful calculating aid, an individual quantum of light had to be able to knock an electron out of the metal—this can only happen if that quantum has sufficient energy, which means that the light has a short wavelength.

DRILL-DOWN | Einstein began his 1905 paper explaining the photoelectric effect by pointing out "a profound formal difference" between the way physicists approach matter and light. Matter was thought of as "being completely determined by the positions and velocities of a very large but nevertheless finite number of atoms and electrons." But light was considered a continuous wave. Einstein was not destroying the wave theory of light, which had "proved itself splendidly in describing purely optical phenomena and will probably never be replaced by another theory." However, he argued that it was not sufficient to deal with the photoelectric effect.

MATTER | *Einstein's Nobel Prize (the 1921 prize, but awarded in 1922) was not for his better-known work on relativity, but "for his services to Theoretical Physics, and especially for his discovery of the law of the photoelectric effect." By 1922, he was deeply uncomfortable with quantum theory and chose to make his Nobel lecture on relativity rather than on light quanta.*

QUANTA
Page 22
QUANTUM ELECTRODYNAMICS
Page 66
EINSTEIN'S OPPOSITION
Page 96

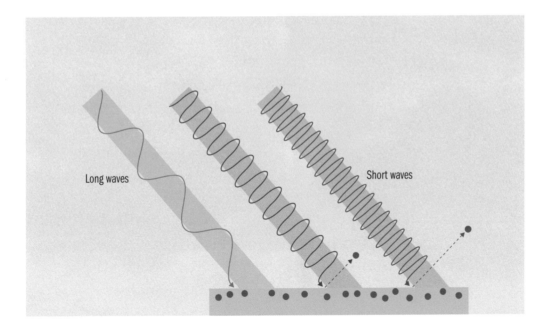

Long waves

Short waves

ATOMIC SPECTRA

THE MAIN CONCEPT | Ever since Isaac Newton's work on light in the seventeenth century, scientists had been aware that white light from the Sun contained a spectrum of colors. However, it was only in 1802, using a combination of a prism and lens to focus the spectrum, that English physicist William Wollaston discovered it had dark lines, or gaps, in it. When better quality spectra became available using a device called a diffraction grating, it became clear that these gaps occurred at similar frequencies to those produced by specific chemical elements when they are heated. It seemed that as light from the Sun was passing through various elements in its outer layers, they were absorbing the same colors as they emit when they are heated. The new science of spectroscopy, which studies these lines, became a useful tool both for astronomers, who could use it to discover the composition of stars, and for chemists, who could identify the elements present in a heated sample. Robert Bunsen's burner, familiar to every chemistry student, was devised to produce a high-temperature flame for spectroscopy. In 1885, Swiss math teacher Johann Balmer noticed something odd about the lines in the spectrum of hydrogen—they weren't randomly positioned, but had a mathematical relationship that fitted a simple formula.

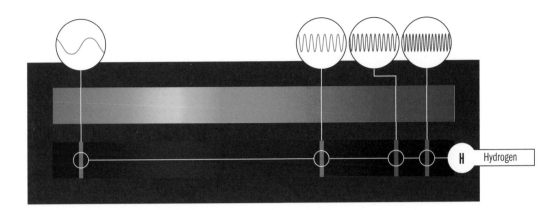

Hydrogen

DRILL-DOWN | The lines in the hydrogen spectrum are spread in wavelength by a value proportional to a simple ratio involving the number of the line plus two. Balmer, who was already sixty years old when he discovered this relationship, produced a formula that matched the wavelength of the known hydrogen lines, and was able to predict a new line, which was later observed. However, Balmer's work and the subsequent development of it by Johannes Rydberg was purely derived from observation. It provided no reason for the relationship between the lines— that would come more than twenty-five years later with Niels Bohr's work on a quantum structure for the atom.

MATTER | *In 1868, French astronomer Jules Janssen noted an unexpected yellow line in the Sun's spectrum, which he assumed was due to sodium. Later the same year, English astronomer Norman Lockyer discovered the same line and correctly deduced it was due to an unknown element, which the chemist Edward Frankland named helium for the Greek name for Sun,* helios.

QUANTA
Page 22
THE QUANTUM ATOM
Page 28
WAVE/PARTICLE DUALITY
Page 30

THE QUANTUM ATOM

THE MAIN CONCEPT | In 1911, New Zealand physicist Ernest Rutherford, working in Manchester, England, had shown that the atom had a small positive nucleus, leaving the electrons somewhere outside. An obvious model was the solar system—but the idea of electrons orbiting (accelerating) around a central nucleus could not work. Young Danish physicist Niels Bohr formulated a quantum atomic model, published in 1913. Inspired by Albert Einstein and Max Planck, Bohr imagined a configuration where electrons occupied only specific orbits, like tracks, around the nucleus. Electrons made instant jumps between the orbits, called quantum leaps. Jumping to a higher orbit required a quantum of energy—absorbing a photon—while jumping down gave off a photon. Bohr discovered Johann Balmer's paper on the pattern in the spectrum of hydrogen and realized that it provided evidence for his own model. When an electron jumped between orbits—Bohr called them "stationary states"— it would always absorb or give off the same amount of energy. And the color (frequency or wavelength) of light was equivalent to the energy of the photon. So elements were expected to give off or absorb energy according to a pattern. Although Bohr's model worked only for hydrogen, it worked beautifully.

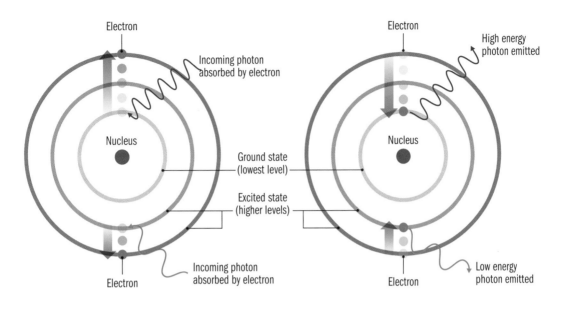

Electron

Incoming photon
absorbed by electron

Nucleus

Ground state
(lowest level)

Excited state
(higher levels)

Incoming photon
absorbed by electron

Electron

Electron

High energy
photon emitted

Nucleus

Electron

Low energy
photon emitted

DRILL-DOWN | A wide range of models were tried by researchers attempting to come up with a structure for the atom, once it was discovered that it had a small positive nucleus. The problem they had was that when an electron is accelerated, it loses energy in the form of electromagnetic radiation. And because acceleration is a change in speed or direction, an orbiting electron constantly accelerates, so it should plunge into the nucleus. An early attempt was made to find a way of positioning the electrons around the nucleus in fixed locations, like the lattice of a crystal. But it was only with Bohr's model that a suitable configuration was found.

QUANTA
Page 22
ATOMIC SPECTRA
Page 26
SCHRÖDINGER'S EQUATION
Page 34

MATTER | *It's tempting when naming a newly discovered structure to borrow terms from elsewhere. Rutherford took the word "nucleus" from biology and applied it to the core of the atom. However, calling electron levels "orbits" would have been misleadingly reminiscent of a solar system. Instead, they became known as shells, with the probability distribution of the locations of the electron called an orbital.*

WAVE/PARTICLE DUALITY

THE MAIN CONCEPT | After Albert Einstein's dramatic assumption that quanta were real, suggesting that light, which had for so long been known to be a wave, had to be treated sometimes as a stream of particles, traditionalist physicists were in shock. So many of the behaviors of light seemed to make sense as the actions of waves and were impossible at the time to explain using particles (it would later prove possible, but originally, quantum particles were still being treated as if they were literal particles, like specks of dust). However, French physicist Louis de Broglie later realized how liberating this concept was. If wave-like light could be regarded as particles, why should quantum particles such as electrons not behave as if they were waves? In 1927, just four years after de Broglie's initial suggestion, two separate experimenters demonstrated that a beam of electrons could produce the kind of diffraction patterns produced by light. Soon after this, electrons were used to duplicate Thomas Young's double-slit experiment, which Young had first used in 1801 to demonstrate the wave nature of light, to show that electron waves interfere with each other to produce an interference pattern. It was no longer realistic to talk solely of waves or particles—there is a strange dual nature to quantum entities.

DRILL-DOWN | If a quantum entity can behave as a wave or a particle, it might seem reasonable that it is a combination of the two. However, experimental physicists found that quantum objects insist on being pinned down if observed. They either appear to be waves or particles, but never both at the same time. So, for example, if the electrons acting as waves to produce an interference pattern are tracked one by one, forcing them to behave as a particle, the pattern disappears. Niels Bohr's Copenhagen group described this either/or nature as complementarity—suggesting a linkage between two principles. This kind of linked structure also came up in Heisenberg's uncertainty principle.

MATTER | *De Broglie (more properly, Louis Victor Pierre Raymond de Broglie) never intended to be a scientist. Born into an aristocratic family, he eventually became the Seventh Duc de Broglie in 1960. De Broglie studied history at the University of Paris, but found an unexpected capability in—and enthusiasm for—math and science, taking a second degree in physics, leading to a distinguished career.*

QUANTA
Page 22
SCHRÖDINGER'S EQUATION
Page 34
THE UNCERTAINTY PRINCIPLE
Page 38

MATRIX MECHANICS

THE MAIN CONCEPT | Although Niels Bohr managed to describe mathematically the behavior of a single electron in a hydrogen atom, it proved difficult to assemble a comprehensive approach to predict how a quantum system of atoms changed over time. As often tends to be the case in science, the initial way around the blockage was to come at the problem from a totally different direction. Bohr's model may have taken a step away from the solar-system concept by requiring quantum leaps, but it was still most naturally visualized as the electrons occupying series of spheres (and later other shapes) around a central nucleus. However, a young German physicist, Werner Heisenberg, threw all this out to start from scratch with a mathematical formulation that matched observation without any attempt to provide an analogy to the real world. As the name suggests, Heisenberg's matrix mechanics involved manipulating matrices—two-dimensional arrays, or rows and columns, of numbers that were well understood by mathematicians, but unfamiliar to physicists. Matrices are odd. For example, we are used to numbers where $A \times B$ is the same as $B \times A$—but this property, known as commutation, does not apply to matrices. Heisenberg's approach developed from Bohr's different states with jumps in between, and disregarded the wave viewpoint of wave/particle duality.

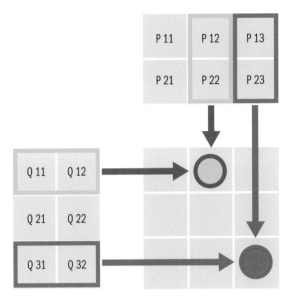

| P 11 | P 12 | P 13 |
| P 21 | P 22 | P 23 |

Q 11	Q 12
Q 21	Q 22
Q 31	Q 32

DRILL-DOWN | Heisenberg's development of matrix mechanics followed the lead of another of the greats of physics, James Clerk Maxwell. In his early career, Maxwell followed the practice of developing models based on analogy. So, for example, one of his earlier models of electromagnetism involved rotating hexagonal objects and tiny, flowing, ball-bearing-like structures. Later, though, he abandoned the analogies in favor of mathematical models that did not involve anything of the world we directly experience. All that existed were the numbers and equations. Many of the great scientists of Maxwell's day, such as Lord Kelvin, could not get their heads around this purely mathematical approach. There was a similar resistance to matrix mechanics.

MATTER | *Present-day physicists are comfortable with models based entirely on mathematics and with concepts such as a quantum field with no tangible equivalent in the world we experience. Just as earlier physicists tended to forget that, for instance, light wasn't a wave or a stream of particles—these were merely models—so modern physicists can forget that their models aren't a description of reality.*

THE QUANTUM ATOM
Page 28
WAVE/PARTICLE DUALITY
Page 30
SCHRÖDINGER'S EQUATION
Page 34

SCHRÖDINGER'S EQUATION

THE MAIN CONCEPT | The young Austrian physicist Erwin Schrödinger came from the opposite direction to Werner Heisenberg. Schrödinger preferred an approach to quantum theory that had more of a sense of the continuous nature of reality than the sharp discontinuities of matrix mechanics. Waves were the classical way to approach something such as light, and had been shown to be useful sometimes even to describe apparently discrete entities such as electrons. This made it seem sensible to Schrödinger to develop a wave equation that described how quantum particles moved and quantum systems of particles evolved. He succeeded, but at a considerable price. The equation appeared to show that, over time, the location of a quantum particle would be "spread out" to cover more and more space. It was Albert Einstein's good friend Max Born who realized why Schrödinger's equation seemed to have such a strange outcome. Instead of representing the location of particle, it gave the probability of finding the particle in any particular location. This meant that with increasing time and distance, there would be a higher chance of finding the particle—but until it was pinpointed, there was only a distribution of probabilities, not an actual location. Later, Schrödinger's equation and matrix mechanics were shown to be interchangeable.

DRILL-DOWN | The original formulation of Schrödinger's equation contained i—a so-called imaginary number that represents the square root of minus one. We know that $1 \times 1 = 1$ and $-1 \times -1 = 1$—there is apparently nothing that multiplied by itself produces -1, but i was arbitrarily introduced to cover this requirement. Imaginary numbers are frequently used in wave physics, as part of a "complex number": combining an ordinary number and an imaginary number is effective at representing a value that varies in two dimensions. However, it's essential when using imaginary numbers that i doesn't feature in a direct description of reality. Luckily, the required outcome turned out to be the square of the equation, losing the imaginary number.

MATTER | *The probabilistic nature of Born's interpretation of Schrödinger's equation was the aspect of quantum physics that turned Einstein against a significant part of physics that he had helped to start. He already disliked the discontinuous nature of the quantum world suggested by Niels Bohr's atomic model, and never accepted that there was not a fixed reality somewhere behind the apparent randomness.*

THE QUANTUM ATOM
Page 28
MATRIX MECHANICS
Page 32
EINSTEIN'S OPPOSITION
Page 96

SCHRÖDINGER'S CAT

THE MAIN CONCEPT | The physicist Erwin Schrödinger was uncomfortable that Max Born's fix of Schrödinger's wave equation meant that probability intruded into reality. This does not only apply to describing the location of a particle as a probability distribution rather than a particular position. For example, if a particle has a property (such as quantum spin) that could be in one of two states, there might be, say, a fifty percent probability of one state and a fifty percent probability of another. We are used to saying this is the case with a tossed coin before we look at it. But after the toss, the coin is in one state (heads or tails) with one hundred percent probability—we just don't know what that state is. By contrast, the quantum particle before observation is in a superposition of states, often described as being in both states at once. There is no hidden reality. To illustrate how ridiculous this seemed, Schrödinger dreamed up a thought experiment. A cat is hidden in a box, its life dependent on the state of a quantum particle. If the particle is in one state, the cat is alive. But in a second state, a detector releases a poisonous gas, killing the cat. Before observation, with the particle in a superposition of states, the cat is both dead and alive simultaneously.

DRILL-DOWN | Many physicists argue that Schrödinger's cat is meaningless as a problem to be solved, because the idea that the particle is in both states at once when in superposition is misleading. When a particle's state is probabilistic, they argue, it isn't in both states at once, but rather there is no state. All that exists are the probabilities, and it is only at the time when the particle's state is observed that it gains a value. The same goes for a particle with a spread-out location—it's not that it is everywhere at once, but rather that it doesn't have a location until it is checked. Up to then, only probabilities exist.

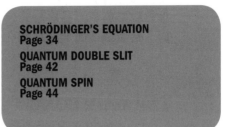

SCHRÖDINGER'S EQUATION
Page 34

QUANTUM DOUBLE SLIT
Page 42

QUANTUM SPIN
Page 44

MATTER | *Schrödinger's cat has become an iconic representation of the oddity of quantum physics. Although few physicists take it seriously, the cat has been referenced in the titles of many papers from "Schrödinger's Cat is now Fat" to "There's More than One Way to Skin Schrödinger's Cat." But Schrödinger's original paper gave the thought experiment only one paragraph in a fifteen-page document.*

THE UNCERTAINTY PRINCIPLE

THE MAIN CONCEPT | After Schrödinger's cat, the best-known concept from quantum physics is Werner Heisenberg's uncertainty principle. It is often used by nonscientists to suggest that everything is fuzzy and unknowable, but like the probabilistic aspects of Schrödinger's equation, the uncertainty principle is a mathematically precise relationship, putting a limit on our ability to know particular values. The uncertainty principle links pairs of properties of quantum systems of particles—momentum (mass multiplied by velocity) and position, or energy and time duration, for example. The uncertainty principle states that the more accurately we know one of the paired properties, the less we can know about the other. So, for example, if we know exactly where a quantum particle is, it could have any momentum. Similarly, if we can pin it down to a precise, short timescale, it could have any of a range of energies. The uncertainty principle is important in understanding the nature of the quantum particles that make up matter. It leads, for example, to the idea that we cannot have quantum particles that are entirely at rest—because if that were the case, both their location and their momentum could be determined. In its turn, this implies that it's impossible to reach absolute zero temperature, where particles should be motionless.

DRILL-DOWN | When Heisenberg first came up with the uncertainty principle, he made an error in describing it. In a lecture, he used an example of a microscope, saying that when we use light to look at a quantum particle, it would be impossible to be sure of both the momentum and the location of the particle because the light bouncing off it would influence it. Niels Bohr, who was in the audience, tore Heisenberg's argument apart, because it seemed to imply that it was the act of observing that set up the uncertainty—but the uncertainty is a fundamental aspect of quantum particles whether or not they are observed.

MATTER | *An impressive result of the uncertainty principle is the scale of the Large Hadron Collider (LHC) at CERN near Geneva, Switzerland. Particle accelerators don't have to be big—early ones were desktop devices. However, the work done at the LHC requires measurements with incredibly detailed positional accuracy. That means pushing up momentum levels, requiring vast devices to give the particle beams sufficient energy.*

WAVE/PARTICLE DUALITY
Page 30
MATRIX MECHANICS
Page 32
PROBABILITY REIGNS
Page 54

THE EXCLUSION PRINCIPLE

THE MAIN CONCEPT | Austrian Wolfgang Pauli is likely the least familiar of the second generation of quantum physicists, but gave his name to a fundamental feature of quantum physics and the quantum model of the atom. When Niels Bohr first created his quantum atomic model in 1913, it was effective only for hydrogen. As more and more electrons were added to the model for the heavier atoms, the concept broke down. Gilbert Lewis, the chemist behind the idea of the covalent bond, suggested there was something about atomic structure that made even numbers of electrons in a shell around the nucleus more stable, with eight electrons, which he associated with the corners of a cube, particularly robust. Nine years after creating his initial model, Bohr came up with an enhanced version where each shell had a specific capacity—two electrons in the inner shell, then eight, then eighteen, and so on. Pauli postulated a logic behind Bohr's structure. This was that an electron's state is defined by four different properties. One is the energy level—which shell the electron is in. The others are momentum, angular momentum, and position. The exclusion principle says that no two electrons in the same quantum system of particles can have all four properties identical.

DRILL-DOWN | The exclusion principle is responsible for most of the workings of chemistry. It defines how electrons are arranged in shells around atoms, and so how they will react with other chemical elements. Reactions depend on the electrons and available spaces in the outermost occupied shell— so, for instance, the noble gases such as helium and neon rarely react with other elements because the noble gases have full outer shells. The exclusion principle also has a major effect on the availability of electrons for conducting electricity and for making some elements semiconductors, and for the nature of matter itself, because it is the electron structure that gives an atom its size.

MATTER | *Particles such as the electron, the proton, and the neutron, obeying the Pauli exclusion principle, are called fermions after Enrico Fermi. They aren't called paulions, because the mathematics describing their behavior is Fermi–Dirac statistics.*

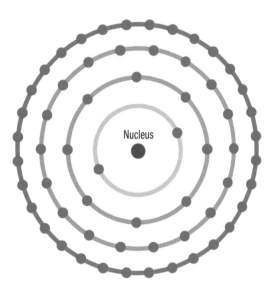

Nucleus

QUANTUM DOUBLE SLIT

THE MAIN CONCEPT | In 1801, English polymath Thomas Young showed light behaved as a wave by sending it through slits toward a screen, where a distinctive pattern of fringes showed that a wave phenomenon called interference had occurred. But if a light beam behaved as a collection of photon particles, each photon would go through one slit or the other, so the expectation would just be to see a blob of light on the screen corresponding to each slit. However, Schrödinger's equation got around this problem by reintroducing the idea of light as waves, and giving values for waves of probability—it is these probability waves that interfere with each other to cause the interference pattern. As technology improved, it became possible to set up a double-slit experiment in which photons were sent one at a time through the experiment. Obviously, a single photon does not have enough energy to produce a useful outcome. But over time, as each photon hits the screen, a picture builds up of the distribution—and the result is the familiar dark and light fringes caused by the interference of probability waves. If any attempt is made to determine which slit the particle went through by using a detector, the interference pattern disappears, and two blobs are produced on the screen.

DRILL-DOWN | The interaction of waves of light demonstrated in Young's double-slit experiment can also be seen when two pebbles are dropped in still water near to each other. When the waves from the pebbles interact with each other, two things can happen. If the waves are in phase with one another—rising or falling at the same time—they reinforce each other. This corresponds to the light fringes seen on the screen in the double-slit experiment. But waves that are out of phase with one another—rising and falling in opposition—cancel each other out, which corresponds to the dark fringes in the double-slit experiment.

WAVE/PARTICLE DUALITY
Page 30
SCHRÖDINGER'S EQUATION
Page 34
COLLAPSING WAVE FUNCTIONS
Page 56

MATTER | *The experiment showing that light was a wave was influenced by a study of how temperature influences the formation of dewdrops. Using a candle to observe a mist of water droplets, Young noticed that the light formed colored rings when it hit a nearby white surface. He wondered if interference between light waves could be responsible, and devised his double-slit experiment.*

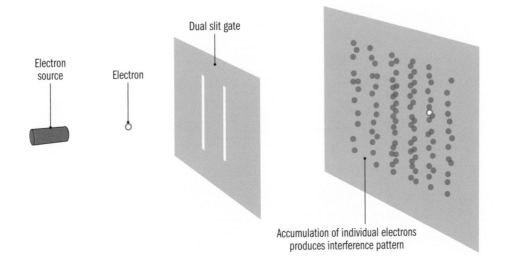

Electron source

Electron

Dual slit gate

Accumulation of individual electrons produces interference pattern

QUANTUM SPIN

THE MAIN CONCEPT | One of the essential properties of a quantum particle is its "spin." This was named because of assumed similarities with angular momentum—the amount of "oomph" with which a normal object spins. This was a natural analogy because many things we experience in the physical world spin around, such as planets on their axes, and the property that came to be known as quantum spin was involved with what were originally thought of as electrons orbiting an atom like a solar system. However, quantum spin does not actually involve anything rotating—the name is just as much an arbitrary term as later quantum terminology such as the "colors" used to describe the interaction of quarks. Spin is one of the four properties of an electron that define its state in atomic orbitals, and was involved in the formulation of the Pauli exclusion principle. This is a purely quantum phenomenon. When the spin of a particle is measured in any particular direction, it will be in either an "up" or "down" state. Before that measurement is made, the particle will usually be in a superposition of the states—just as the location of a particle is simply a collection of probabilities, here we have only the combined probability of being up and down.

THE EXCLUSION PRINCIPLE
Page 40

THE EPR PAPER
Page 98

BELL'S INEQUALITY
Page 100

DRILL-DOWN | The "size" of a quantum particle's spin cannot vary—spin is an inherent property of the type of particle—underlining the way that spin does not involve rotating in a conventional way. Only the probability of the detected direction of spin varies. Each particle has what is known as a spin quantum number, which describes the amount of spin it must have: these can only have values of 0, ½, 1, ³⁄₂, and so on. Fermion particles such as electrons and quarks have half-integer spins, while bosons such as photons have whole-number spins. Quantum spin later became a valuable property when exploring other quantum phenomena such as entanglement.

MATTER | *Quantum spin was first directly demonstrated in the Stern–Gerlach experiment. In this, neutral particles were sent through a varying magnetic field. The expectation was that the literal spin of the particles would produce a range of deflections depending on field strength, but in practice, each particle was deflected either up or down by a fixed amount—the spin was quantized.*

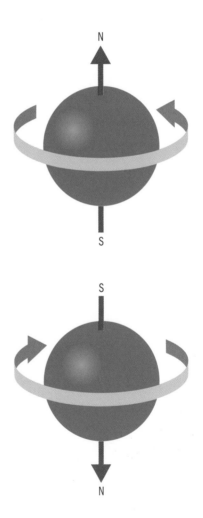

"The theory of quantum electrodynamics describes Nature as absurd from the point of view of common sense. And it agrees fully with experiment. So I hope you can accept Nature as She is—absurd."

RICHARD FEYNMAN,
QED: THE STRANGE THEORY OF LIGHT AND MATTER (1985)

2
QUANTUM BEHAVIOR

QUANTUM THEORY MATURES

In the 1920s, inspired work by Bohr, Heisenberg, and Schrödinger took quantum physics from a limited fix for a problem to a detailed description of quantum systems (anything from a single quantum particle to a whole collection of them). At this stage, however, quantum theory had limitations. Some physicists struggled with its probabilistic nature. When a particle was observed—for example, when a photon hit the screen in the double-slit experiment—it clearly had a specific location. There had to be some kind of mechanism to change the particle from a collection of probabilities to having an observed position. This mechanism, known as wave function collapse, was mysterious, and some felt there had to be a better interpretation. Physicists now prefer a concept known as decoherence, which describes the same process but avoids the need for a wave function to collapse.

As well as getting a better understanding of this mechanism, physicists were pushing the boundaries of application of quantum theory. Many quantum particles travel at high speeds, which made it necessary to bring in the special theory of relativity. Toward the end of the 1920s, English physicist Paul Dirac found a solution combining the original equations with relativity. But to make his new equation work, Dirac had to imagine an unlikely scenario featuring an infinite sea of electrons, all with negative amounts of energy. Strange though this seemed, the concept was testable, as it predicted the existence of a new kind of matter.

Antimatter and quantum fields

This "antimatter" consists of particles that are nearly identical to existing ones, but have opposite values of some properties, for example, electrical charge. A few years later, the first antimatter particles, positrons (also known as antielectrons), were discovered. In time, antimatter proved to be a fundamental player in the creation of the universe. With sufficient energy, photons can transform into a pair of particles—one matter, one antimatter. It is thought that it was from this process that the matter in the universe came into being. As often seems to be the case with quantum theory, the solution to one problem caused another. In this case, it is not yet fully answered: what happened to all the antimatter in the universe, as it now seems to be very rare?

At the same time as these developments, quantum physics was being transformed from a regime that primarily dealt with particles or waves to a field theory. Field theories had emerged in the late nineteenth century when trying to explain electricity and magnetism. The approach moves away from individual entities such as particles and waves, to a field, which is something that fills all of space and has a time-dependent value that could be different at each point in space. It's easy to get hung up on worrying about whether light or an electron really is a particle or a wave or a disturbance in a quantum field. What we need to remember is that each of these is a model—a way of describing reality that allows us to make calculations and predictions. We are not saying that light, for example, is any of these, but each model is particularly useful in some circumstances, and the quantum field theory approach has tended to be particularly valuable for many calculations.

The intersection of light and matter

By the 1940s, the burgeoning quantum field theory had become quantum electrodynamics, or QED. This is an approach that describes not just the behavior of individual particles (or waves, or disturbances in quantum field—it can just be easier to say "particles"), but also of the interaction between them. Crucially, it covers all the circumstances where light interacts with matter, which occurs not only in the more obvious examples of a photon being absorbed or emitted by an electron in an atom, but also with any electromagnetic interaction between matter particles.

As physicists gained a better understanding of these kinds of quantum interaction, they were able to predict and explain the explicitly quantum phenomena that go on around us. They used the new quantum approach to show how, for example, a photon that hits a sheet of glass "decides" whether to reflect off it or pass through it. They also predicted and then demonstrated a process known as quantum tunneling, where a particle gets through an apparently unsurmountable barrier by simply appearing on the other side. This apparently highly unlikely process is essential for life on Earth. And tunneling even provides a mechanism by which a photon can apparently travel faster than the ultimate speed limit, the speed of light.

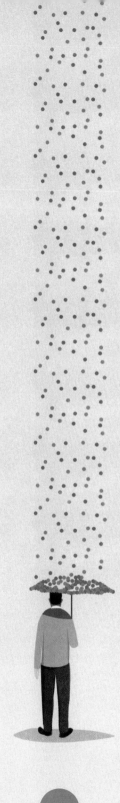

BIOGRAPHIES

ALBERT EINSTEIN (1879–1955)

The most famous scientist of modern times, Albert Einstein was born on March 14, 1879 in Ulm, Germany. From an early age, he struggled with authority—while he enjoyed some subjects at school, he couldn't see the point of others, and by the age of fifteen, he had given up his German citizenship to avoid conscription. After gaining a mediocre degree at the Zurich Technical College, he could not get a position in academia, so became a patent clerk. In 1905, while working at the patent office, Einstein wrote four groundbreaking papers, including one establishing special relativity, one showing that $E = mc^2$, and another showing the foundations of quantum physics, based on the photoelectric effect, which won him the Nobel Prize in Physics in 1922. After the publication of his masterpiece, the general theory of relativity, in 1915, which brings gravity into relativity, Einstein became a public figure. From this time onward, he spent considerable effort trying to undermine the quantum physics he had helped start, as he was unhappy with its dependence on probability. In the 1930s, Einstein left Germany as anti-Jewish sentiment grew, and worked at the Institute of Advanced Study in Princeton in the United States until his death in 1955 at the age of seventy-six.

WOLFGANG PAULI (1900–1958)

Born in Vienna, Austria, on April 25, 1900, Wolfgang Pauli has not achieved the same level of fame as some of the big names in quantum physics—but the principle named for him, the Pauli exclusion principle, won him the Nobel Prize in Physics in 1945. The exclusion principle is essential in providing a quantum explanation for everything from the chemical behavior of atoms to neutron stars and black holes. It was while lecturing at the University of Hamburg in the 1920s that Pauli made his most noteworthy contributions to quantum physics. However, his exclusion principle and his work on quantum spin would not be his only significant contributions to physical science—it was Pauli, for example, who predicted the existence of a new particle, later called the neutrino, which is important in understanding how nuclear reactions work. As a side interest, he worked with the psychiatrist Carl Jung, both as a patient and in helping Jung formulate his theories. Pauli moved to the United States in 1940, but returned after the war to Switzerland, which had been his home since the late 1920s. He died in Zurich in 1958, aged fifty-eight.

PAUL DIRAC (1902–1984)

Born in Bristol, England, on August 8, 1902, Paul Dirac is probably the most important physicist of the quantum age that hardly anyone has heard of. Dirac studied electrical engineering and mathematics at the University of Bristol before moving to Cambridge, England, which would be his academic home until his retirement. There, Dirac focused on relativity and quantum physics, combining the two by expanding Schrödinger's equation to take in particles moving at high speeds. The equation Dirac produced required electrons to be able to have negative energies—which meant there should be no minimum energy level, but electrons could plunge lower and lower. As this wasn't observed to be true, Dirac suggested instead that an infinite sea of negative-energy electrons filled all available spaces, so the only observed electrons had positive energy. This model predicted a different kind of particle—an antielectron, or positron, which was discovered experimentally a few years later. Dirac's work won the Nobel Prize in Physics in 1933. He also made major steps forward in combining the main approaches to quantum physics and bringing electromagnetism into the fold. Apart from his work, he was best known for having limited social skills. Dirac died in Tallahassee, Florida, in 1984, aged eighty-two.

RICHARD FEYNMAN (1918–1988)

Richard Feynman, born on May 11, 1918, was anything but the stereotype of a socially inept physicist. Brash and an enthusiastic communicator, he was something of a showman throughout his career. During World War II, when working on the Manhattan Project, he was known as much for his spare-time activities of breaking into safes and secure filing cabinets to demonstrate the limitations of security as he was for his contributions to the physics of nuclear weapons. Shortly after the war, he made his breakthrough work in fundamental quantum physics—specifically, the quantum physics of the interaction of light with matter, and matter with matter. Along with Julian Schwinger and Sin'Itiro Tomonaga, he won the Nobel Prize in Physics in 1965 for his development of this quantum electrodynamics, or QED. One of Feynman's most significant contributions was the development of Feynman diagrams, which help both to explain and to enable calculations on QED interactions. Feynman went on to become a popular physics communicator, and discovered the cause of the 1986 space shuttle Challenger crash as a member of the investigating commission, dramatically demonstrating his theory on live television. Feynman died in 1988, aged seventy.

TIMELINE

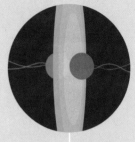

THE DIRAC EQUATION
Paul Dirac produces an equation that describes the behavior of electrons at relativistic (near the speed of light) speeds. This is necessary to provide an effective quantum model of the atom. To make his equation work, Dirac has to postulate the existence of a sea of negative-energy electrons, which leads to the concept of antimatter.

1927

1928

1932

QUANTUM TUNNELING
Quantum tunneling, where a quantum particle's probabilistic location enables it to pass through an otherwise unsurmountable barrier, is first observed by Friedrich Hund and is used in theoretical work the following year by George Gamow. Tunneling would prove essential in explaining the nuclear fusion process in stars.

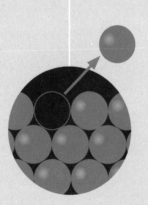

ANTIMATTER
Carl Anderson discovers the first example of antimatter—an antielectron, also known as a positron, discovered in cosmic rays. This positively charged equivalent of an electron was predicted by Paul Dirac's theory, but originally considered unlikely to exist. Antimatter equivalents of all matter particles were later discovered.

QED

Richard Feynman, Julian Schwinger, and Sin'Itiro Tomonaga build on Paul Dirac's work to develop quantum electrodynamics (QED). QED describes how all electromagnetic quantum phenomena take place. As this covers all interactions between light and matter, and between matter and matter, it explains the majority of everyday experience.

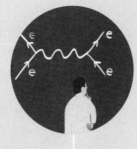

SENDING DATA

Günter Nimtz demonstrates the ability of quantum tunneling to carry information faster than light, using a recording of Mozart's Fortieth Symphony, transmitted at over four times the speed of light. The demonstration at a conference in Snowbird, Utah, is in response to the suggestion that this quantum tunneling could be used to send only random data.

1948   **1948**   **1995**

FEYNMAN DIAGRAMS

Richard Feynman introduces Feynman diagrams, which both illustrate quantum interactions and are used in quantum physics calculations. Showing interactions over time, the diagrams feature straight lines for matter particles and wavy lines for photons. Although apparently simple, the diagrams make it practical to keep track of complex interactions and become universally used.

PROBABILITY REIGNS

THE MAIN CONCEPT | Quantum physics is frequently described as mysterious. As US physicist Michio Kaku commented, "It is often stated that of all the theories proposed in [the twentieth] century, the silliest is quantum theory. Some say that the only thing that quantum theory has going for it, in fact, is that it is unquestionably correct." The reason for this view is that quantum physics says that the components that make up the universe, such as atoms and electrons and photons of light, behave differently from the objects that are made from and interact with these components. If I put a ball somewhere, unless something moves it, it will stay there. If I throw a ball, it follows a predictable trajectory. And if I reflect light off a flat mirror, it will reflect at an angle equal to the angle at which it arrives. But quantum physics tells us that the particles making up the ball, the light, and the mirror are all subject to probability. When we look at a reflection in a mirror, for example, quantum theory tells us a photon has a probability of reflecting at every possible angle. Usually, most probabilities cancel out, but if we remove parts of the mirror that allow for this cancelation, light reflects at unexpected angles.

DRILL-DOWN | The probabilistic nature of quantum particles is sometimes taken as meaning that quantum behavior is random and unpredictable, but physicists are quick to point out that the probabilities themselves are not random, but deterministic. So, for example, take the decaying particle used in the Schrödinger's cat thought experiment. Probability enters into the situation because we don't know—we cannot know—when the particle will decay. After a while without being observed, the particle will be in a superposition of decayed and nondecayed states. But we can specify exactly what the half-life of the particle is: a fixed period of time during which the particle has a 50/50 chance of decaying.

SCHRÖDINGER'S CAT
Page 36

THE UNCERTAINTY PRINCIPLE
Page 38

QUANTUM DOUBLE SLIT
Page 42

MATTER | *Take a CD or DVD and tilt it at an angle. Rainbow patterns will appear on the surface. This is a direct result of the probabilistic nature of quantum physics. Optical disks store information as tiny pits in a reflective metal foil. The pits stop some of the possible routes for the light, producing reflections at unexpected angles, which vary by wavelength, causing the rainbow patterns.*

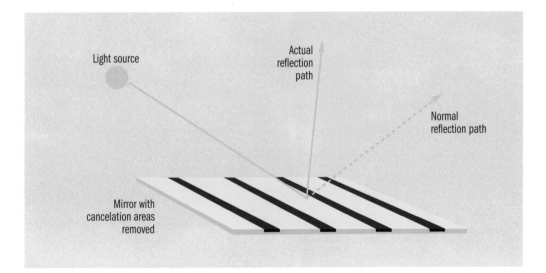

Light source

Actual reflection path

Normal reflection path

Mirror with cancelation areas removed

COLLAPSING WAVE FUNCTIONS

THE MAIN CONCEPT | Perhaps the most controversial aspect of the original formulation of quantum theory among physicists themselves was the idea of collapsing wave functions. According to Schrödinger's equation, the state of a quantum system was described by a wave function, which showed, for example, different probabilities of finding a particle at various locations. This wave function evolved over time, with the different probabilities spreading out to encompass wider areas. But if the particle were observed, the wave function was said to "collapse," leaving the particle at the position where it was observed with one hundred percent probability. Some struggled with just what such a collapse meant; what was changing to represent this collapse? There was no mechanism provided—somehow the system went from a superposition of possible states (for example, locations) to occupying a single one—because that was what it did. But there was no suggestion as to how. Others dismissed wave function collapse as an issue (and still do)—their viewpoint, summed up as "shut up and calculate," was that as long as the equations matched what was observed, it was pointless speculating about what was "really" happening. We would never be able to directly connect to reality, and so there was little point worrying about the nature of wave function collapse.

DRILL-DOWN | Traditionally, we make a clear distinction between the observer and the experiment. But it is possible to consider them as forming a single system. Wave function collapse is arguably a relative term, dependent on isolating the quantum system being observed. However, whatever appears to cause the wave function to collapse—observing a particle, say—is part of a larger quantum system incorporating both the experiment and the cause. In this larger system, there is no collapse because, overall, the whole system of the experiment and its environment continues in principle to follow Schrödinger's equation (in practice, the complete system is usually too complex to make a calculation of its evolution through time).

MATTER | *We are unable to directly access reality, a problem that has plagued the philosophy of science ever since the time of Immanuel Kant. In the eighteenth century, Kant distinguished between the actual reality of nature—the "Ding an sich"—and our observations, which could only ever be interpretations of sensory inputs rather than a true description of "the thing itself."*

SCHRÖDINGER'S EQUATION
Page 34
DECOHERENCE
Page 58
THE COPENHAGEN INTERPRETATION
Page 88

DECOHERENCE

THE MAIN CONCEPT | Those who were most uncomfortable with the notion of wave function collapse developed a new, subtle variant of the concept, known as decoherence. In effect, decoherence makes use of the approach where we take in the wider system, including more than the part of the system that is said to collapse, but without taking on the impossible complication of including everything in the universe that could influence the experiment in the calculation. Decoherence envisages that the experiment—for example, a quantum particle's behavior—does not actually undergo wave function collapse, but that the interaction of the particle's wave function and that of something causing the apparent collapse—for example, when it interacts with another particle—produces a combined effect that makes it look as if the wave function has collapsed. The practical explanation of this is called quantum entanglement— the particle becomes "entangled" with the other particle, their properties interacting, and ceases to act as a totally independent system. The advantage of decoherence over straight wave function collapse is that it does provide an explanation for apparent collapse occurring, rather than simply stating it as the way things are. Alternative explanations of quantum theory, notably the "many worlds" interpretation use decoherence rather than collapse.

DRILL-DOWN | The more a piece of technology makes direct use of quantum states, the bigger the problem from decoherence. For example, the emerging field of spintronics makes use of an electron's spin as well as its charge. And many teams are working on quantum computers, where the equivalent of the 0/1 values of a traditional computer bit are the superposed quantum states of a particle. If the particles used in these devices interact with their surroundings, decoherence occurs, and the quantum calculations fail. One of the main reasons it has taken forty years to get quantum computers from theory to practicality is the difficulty of avoiding decoherence over any practical timescale.

MATTER | *The concept of decoherence depends on an aspect of quantum physics known as entanglement, a term that was introduced by Erwin Schrödinger when speaking at the Cambridge Philosophical Society in 1935. Because entanglement requires quantum particles to be able to interact at a distance, Einstein referred to it as "spükhafte Fernwirkungen," literally spooky actions at a distance.*

COLLAPSING WAVE FUNCTIONS
Page 56

THE BOHM INTERPRETATION
Page 90

THE EPR PAPER
Page 98

DIRAC'S EQUATION

THE MAIN CONCEPT | Schrödinger's equation was a huge step forward for quantum physics, describing how a quantum system evolves with time. However, it did not include the influence of the special theory of relativity, where fast moving objects behave differently from expectation. British physicist Paul Dirac in the 1920s formulated a relativistic equivalent of Schrödinger's equation. It built on Bohr's model of the quantum atom, which had worked effectively only with a single electron, and only at low energies where relativistic effects could be ignored. Dirac's equation made it possible to deal with fast moving electrons and more complex atoms, producing results that matched observation. Unfortunately, the Dirac equation only worked if it were possible for electrons to have both positive and negative energy—and no one was sure what a negative-energy electron would be like. If electrons could occupy negative-energy levels, electrons around atoms would continually leap down lower into the negative, giving off energy in the form of light. This should go on indefinitely—there is no bottom to this negative-energy "well." Dirac fixed this by imagining that there was already an infinite sea of negative-energy electrons, which filled up all the spaces that were available. This meant that all observed electrons had to have positive energy, because there were available spaces only in the positive levels. Half of reality was totally occupied, with what was observed taking place in the other half.

DRILL-DOWN | When an electron absorbs a photon, it undergoes a quantum leap, jumping up to a higher energy level. This process applies just as much to negative-energy electrons as positive-energy electrons. What remains is a gap, which could be filled by a positive-energy electron falling into it. The missing negative-energy electron proved mathematically identical to a present positive-energy particle, identical to an electron but positively charged. Such a particle—the positron or antielectron—was first observed a few years later. If positive-energy electrons dropped into gaps, they would disappear, producing photons. Again, this was observed to happen: when an electron and a positron collide, they annihilate, giving off energy.

THE QUANTUM ATOM
Page 28
SCHRÖDINGER'S EQUATION
Page 34
ANTIMATTER
Page 64

MATTER | *Conversations with Dirac were notoriously awkward, often involving remarks that were monosyllabic or strange. He tended to introduce his wife, for instance, as "Wigner's sister" (referring to her brother, Hungarian physicist, Eugene Wigner). It perhaps didn't help that at home, his mother spoke English, but his father only French. He once remarked that when young, he had thought men and women spoke different languages.*

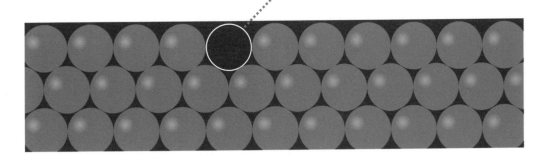

QUANTUM FIELD THEORY

THE MAIN CONCEPT | Although Schrödinger's and Dirac's equations proved immensely valuable in explaining the behavior of quantum particles, they could not provide a useful description of the wider interaction of quantum particles—for example, of light and matter. The classical description of light was based on field theory—started as a descriptive concept by Michael Faraday and given mathematical rigor by James Clerk Maxwell. The underlying concept of a field was a hypothetical "something" filling the universe, which could have a different value at every point in space and time. A two-dimensional equivalent would be a contour map, providing the two-dimensional space of the map with a value at each point. Fields made it possible to explain phenomena such as electricity and magnetism without resorting to action at a distance. Instead, for example, a magnet produced a traveling distortion in the field that was felt remotely. Light became an interaction between variations in the electrical and magnetic fields. Quantum field theory adds on the quantum nature of small-scale phenomena. It was first employed by Paul Dirac and required the values in the field to be quantized. In a quantum field description of reality, light, for example, was a traveling fluctuation in a field—and because it was a quantum field, those fluctuations were made up of photons.

DRILL-DOWN | Some physicists consider reality to be nothing more than a collection of overlapping quantum fields, known as "the bulk." In this picture, all phenomena are simply fluctuations in the various quantum fields. It certainly is one way of representing the universe, although it comes across as stark and mathematical, just as did Heisenberg's matrix mechanics. Quantum fields are excellent ways of representing reality and performing mathematical manipulations to represent quantum actions, but it's important that we do not forget that, as was the case with waves and particles, quantum fields are not reality—they are models that enable us to interpret what we can detect of reality better.

WAVE/PARTICLE DUALITY
Page 30

SCHRÖDINGER'S EQUATION
Page 34

QUANTUM ELECTRODYNAMICS
Page 66

MATTER | *The concept of a field strongly echoes the older idea of the ether, an invisible "something" filling all of space. When it was understood light sometimes behaved like a wave, it was difficult to explain what was doing the waving in empty space. The ether filled the gap. However, the ether was thought to be a substance, rather than a property of space itself.*

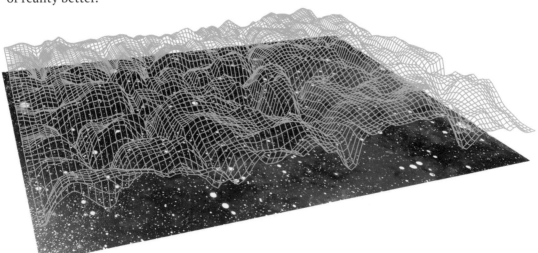

ANTIMATTER

THE MAIN CONCEPT | The concept of antimatter emerged from Paul Dirac's prediction that there should be negative-energy electrons, which he "fixed" by assuming there was an infinite sea of these electrons, filling all available negative-energy gaps. However, there was nothing to stop one of these electrons absorbing a photon and jumping up to a positive-energy level, leaving behind a hole in the negative-energy sea. This absence of a negatively charged, negative-energy electron proved to be identical to a positively charged, positive-energy positron, or antielectron. Within a few years of Dirac's theory, the positron was discovered in cosmic rays—high-energy sprays of particles from space. The positron had the same mass as an electron, but the opposite charge. One of the predictions from the Dirac sea was that an ordinary, positive-energy electron could drop down into a negative-energy hole. If that happened, the electron would disappear, leaving only energy in the form of photons. This meant that if the matter and antimatter particles came together, they would annihilate each other, turning into pure energy. A few years later, an alternative approach to reaching Dirac's equation meant that the infinite sea was no longer necessary—but the concept of antimatter it spawned is still going strong.

QUANTUM FIELD THEORY
Page 62

DIRAC'S EQUATION
Page 60

QUANTUM ELECTRODYNAMICS
Page 66

DRILL-DOWN | Each matter particle has an equivalent antiparticle. The distinctions between particle and antiparticle are clearer with a charged particle—so, for example, an antiproton has the same mass as a proton, but a negative charge. The CERN laboratory has produced antihydrogen atoms, where a positron orbits an antiproton—but electrically neutral antiparticles such as antihydrogen are difficult to handle because they cannot be constrained by electromagnetic fields in the way charged particles can, so come into contact with ordinary matter and get annihilated. Neutral particles such as neutrons also have antiparticles that vary in other quantum numbers, while photons and similar particles are sometimes considered to be their own antiparticle.

MATTER | *Photons can convert to matter ($E=mc^2$), producing equal quantities of matter and antimatter. Since all the matter in the universe came from photons, it is strange that little antimatter is seen. It has been speculated that the antimatter is somehow separate from the rest of the universe or, more likely, an asymmetry between matter and antimatter resulted in more matter being created.*

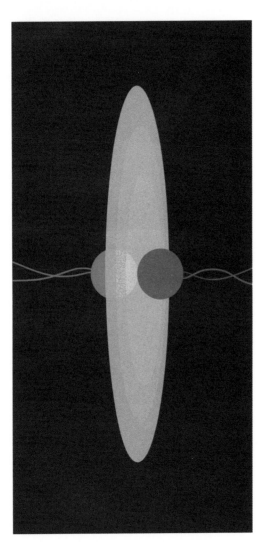

QUANTUM ELECTRODYNAMICS

THE MAIN CONCEPT | Quantum electrodynamics, or QED, describes the interaction of matter with matter, and matter with light, all dependent on electromagnetism. Three individuals developed QED independently just after World War II (winning the 1965 Nobel Prize for it)— Richard Feynman and Julian Schwinger in the United States and Sin'Itiro Tomonaga in Japan. Feynman loved to highlight how far removed QED was from everyday experience, with particles probabilistically taking every possible path. He said: "It is my task to persuade you not to turn away because you don't understand it. You see, my physics students don't understand it either. This is because I don't understand it. Nobody does." But strange though the theory was, it worked. Although QED is a quantum field theory, for practical purposes, Feynman's approach treated the disturbances in the quantum field as particles, and was able to show that all the behavior of light and matter that seemed to imply the existence of waves could be handled using quantum particles that have a property called phase that changes direction with time. QED was immensely powerful, but it had one problem that would cause a significant challenge. Because of the way it added up possibilities over every possible outcome, it was easy to end up with an infinite result.

DRILL-DOWN | QED explains many everyday interactions. There are the interactions of light and matter, where a photon pushes an electron to a higher energy level, or is given off when an electron jumps down. But there are also many more interactions between matter particles, often as a result of never-seen "virtual" photons, carrying the electromagnetic force. For example, when you sit on a chair, your atoms do not touch it. Instead, there is an electromagnetic interplay between the charged particles in your body and those of the chair, provided by an intense exchange of photons. This enables you to float above the chair—otherwise your atoms would pass straight through it.

MATTER | *Scientific theories can make inaccurate predictions. The current calculation for a phenomenon called vacuum energy is many trillions of times bigger than reality. By comparison, QED makes accurate predictions—the agreement with tests measuring the strength of electromagnetic interaction between particles is within one ten billionth, equivalent to measuring the distance from New York to Los Angeles to a hair's width.*

QUANTUM FIELD THEORY
Page 62

RENORMALIZATION
Page 68

FEYNMAN DIAGRAMS
Page 70

RENORMALIZATION

THE MAIN CONCEPT | What do you do when you have a wonderfully effective theory that throws up infinite results? The power of QED is in the way it adds up all the possible ways of getting from the start to the end of a particle interaction. It might seem this will result in infinite outcomes because there are infinite possibilities. However, many options cancel each other out, or are so small that an infinite series of them converges. For example, the infinite series $1 + \frac{1}{2} + \frac{1}{4} + \frac{1}{8} + \frac{1}{16} \ldots$ adds up to 2. But some series diverge—the total sum of $1 + \frac{1}{2} + \frac{1}{3} + \frac{1}{4} + \frac{1}{5} \ldots$ is infinite. In QED's particle interactions, there can be self-action, where a particle interacts with its own electromagnetic field and those around it to produce an infinite outcome. Clearly, in the real world, these infinities do not exist. The solution was renormalization. If, for example, QED predicted the mass of a particle should be infinite, it was replaced with the observed value. With this, the other results from QED worked perfectly. Renormalization was initially called a fudge, but was eventually considered to reflect a physical process—where something physical resets the value that would otherwise be infinite.

DRILL-DOWN | Heisenberg's uncertainty principle predicts that, because energy in a location in space could have any of a range of values over very short periods of time, pairs of "virtual" particles will constantly be popping into existence and disappearing again. Think of an electron sitting in apparently empty space—in QED, it is necessary to include any potential interaction with these virtual particles around the electron. Similarly, if an electron gives off a photon, there is a recoil effect—which results in the electron's electromagnetic field acting on itself. The result of this combined assault on the electron is a prediction of values for mass, for example, that goes to infinity.

THE QUANTUM ATOM
Page 28

QUANTUM ELECTRODYNAMICS
Page 66

FEYNMAN DIAGRAMS
Page 70

MATTER | *Zeno's paradox of Achilles and the tortoise shows an infinite series adding to a finite value. In a race, Achilles gives the tortoise a lead. By the time he reaches where the tortoise was, it has moved on. When he gets to its new destination, it is further ahead. And so on. But in reality, Achilles wins: the infinite set of distances adds to a finite value.*

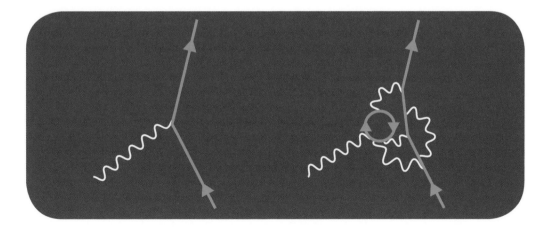

FEYNMAN DIAGRAMS

THE MAIN CONCEPT | Central to Richard Feynman's approach to QED was the Feynman diagram, which has become a staple of quantum physics. The diagrams show how different quantum particles interact, providing a visual version of the mathematical description of an event. Time is shown on one axis of the diagram, while spatial position is shown on the other (there is no fixed standard for which is which)—so they display the progress of particles through time. Straight lines represent matter particles such as electrons, while wiggly lines stand in for photons—whenever two or more lines intersect, the particles are interacting. The diagrams have a dual benefit: they make it easier to see the different options for a particle interaction, but also each part of the diagram represents a part of the mathematical equations required to calculate the outcome. Because a quantum particle does not simply travel from A to B like a classical particle but has many probabilistic options, multiple diagrams are often required, with the overall outcome, known as the path integral, providing the sum across all possibilities. Feynman diagrams are still widely used today, and have been expanded beyond quantum electrodynamics to take in other quantum particle interactions such as quantum chromodynamics, which deals with strong nuclear-force interactions involving quarks and gluons.

DRILL-DOWN | Antiparticles such as the positron, or antielectron, are treated differently from normal particles in Feynman diagrams. Antiparticles are shown as if they were the equivalent normal matter particle but going backward in time. So, for example, one of the simplest matter/antimatter interactions involves an electron and a positron coming together and annihilating to produce a pair of photons. This is shown with the direction in time arrow on the electron representing the positron running backward from the moment the two particles annihilate. Most physicists regard this "backward in time" direction to be a useful simplification for calculation (hence why it was introduced) rather than a statement of an actual particle's behavior.

QUANTUM FIELD THEORY
Page 62
ANTIMATTER
Page 64
QUANTUM ELECTRODYNAMICS
Page 66

MATTER | *Richard Feynman was so delighted with his diagrams that he had a new 1975 Dodge Tradesman Maxivan painted up with Feynman diagrams and was a popular sight, driving it around the Caltech campus. His license plates also reflected the theme, although because there was a limit of six letters on California plates at the time, he went for QANTUM.*

ZERO-POINT ENERGY

THE MAIN CONCEPT | A remarkable implication of QED and Heisenberg's uncertainty principle is that over short periods of time, the energy in a quantum system varies hugely. This is even true of empty space. Empty space has a positive energy value—known as zero-point energy. This has excited many, who feel it should be possible to make use of this energy. This is particularly appealing in space, as it would mean that spaceships would not need to carry fuel, and it would be possible to constantly apply a low acceleration, building up to immense speeds over time. Zero-point energy enthusiasts also suggest it could provide a limitless power source on Earth. However, there are two distinct problems to be faced. One is that the energy density is very low, so it would struggle to power anything significant. But more importantly, to make use of a certain level of energy, you need somewhere else with lower energy to produce work. But there is nowhere lower than zero-point energy, by definition. It's like trying to make use of the potential energy in the middle of a mountain plateau. Yes, you are high above sea level—but you cannot roll something down and use the energy, because none of your surroundings are lower.

DRILL-DOWN | Although it is unlikely zero-point energy could be harnessed, a phenomenon called the Casimir effect gives small-scale evidence of its presence. This is the impact of zero-point energy on two closely spaced metal plates. The two plates feel a force toward each other. One way of envisioning this is that the random fluctuations in energy will sometimes be enough for matter/ antimatter pairs of particles to briefly pop into existence. When they do, they will cause pressure on the plates—but because the plates are so close together there isn't enough room for this to occur to any significant extent between the plates, so they feel a net inward pressure.

MATTER | *The EmDrive ("radio frequency resonant cavity thruster"), and the "Cannae Drive," named for* Star Trek*'s Scotty's habit of saying "I cannae change the laws of physics," are controversial attempts to produce spaceship thrusters that do not emit propellants. Some suggest these make use of zero-point energy, but as yet there is no definitive evidence that they work at all.*

THE UNCERTAINTY PRINCIPLE
Page 38

QUANTUM FIELD THEORY
Page 62

QUANTUM ELECTRODYNAMICS
Page 66

WINDOWS & BEAM SPLITTERS

THE MAIN CONCEPT | It's easy to consider quantum theory as something limited to the lab. But a glass window provides a demonstration of quantum physics in action, acting as a beam splitter. Stand in a lit room at night looking at the window, and you will see a reflection of the room. But go outside and you see into the room. So, despite some of the light from inside reflecting off the glass back into the room, the rest passes through the glass. This is classic quantum probabilistic behavior. Around five percent of the light reflects back into the room and ninety-five percent passes through. But how does a photon know whether to pass through or reflect? This was a puzzle to Isaac Newton, who believed light was made of particles. Newton thought the effect might be due to imperfections in the surface of the glass—but polishing the glass doesn't make it go away. From a quantum viewpoint, we can see that there are no surface blemishes required to make the split. The photon exists merely as probabilities of passing through or reflecting, producing the statistical result. A sheet of glass isn't a great beam splitter—for experiments, more sophisticated devices involving part-silvered mirrors or prisms, which split light 50/50, are used.

DRILL-DOWN | When light reflects back off window glass, the probability of the photon reflecting from the inner surface depends on the thickness of the glass. Somehow, the photon "knows" how thick the glass is. With a wave-based approach, this is easy to explain as an interaction between waves that pass through the glass and reflect back from the outer surface and those that reflect off the inner surface. But with particles of light, it is only explainable if you take in the nonspecificity of a quantum particle's location, which means it has a probability of already being at the far side of the glass and so can be influenced by its thickness.

MATTER | *We only see the room reflected back from a window at night for the same reason we see stars at night. Stars are always there, but during the day, their weak light is washed out by sunlight. Similarly, we only see the outside view through a window during the day as there is far more light coming through than reflects back.*

SCHRÖDINGER'S EQUATION
Page 34
QUANTUM DOUBLE SLIT
Page 42
BELL'S INEQUALITY
Page 100

TUNNELING

THE MAIN CONCEPT | A very significant quantum effect with an obvious impact on everyday life is quantum tunneling. This is directly linked to the indeterminate location of a quantum particle. If there is a barrier in the particle's way that it does not have the energy to get over or through, a particle would usually be stopped. Think, for instance, of throwing a tennis ball at a wall, or trying to pitch one over a wall that is far higher than you can throw. But if the barrier is relatively thin, thanks to Schrödinger's equation, we know that a quantum particle will have a probability of already being on the other side of the barrier. The wave equation shows the probability of its location spreading out over time—and is unaffected by barriers. It's as if we put a car in a garage and came back to find it had jumped through the wall of the building and was out in the driveway. In a way, "tunneling" is a misnomer as it implies that the particle forces its way through the barrier; in reality, it is already on the other side. This means that the tunneling process is instantaneous—the particle does not take any time to get through the barrier.

DRILL-DOWN | The existence of life on Earth is a dramatic demonstration of the power of quantum tunneling. The Earth would be uninhabitable without the Sun, which provides us with both light and warmth. And the process powering the Sun depends on tunneling. Inside a star, gravitational pressure forces positively charged protons together. They undergo nuclear fusion, where a number of protons combine to make helium, generating energy. But this process shouldn't work. The electromagnetic repulsion between the positively charged protons is so strong, they cannot get close enough to fuse. It's only because, as quantum particles, they can tunnel through the barrier of the repulsion that the Sun works and we're alive.

MATTER | *There is little danger of finding that your car has tunneled through the wall of your garage and appeared on the driveway. The chances of any particular particle tunneling are very small—and with the vast numbers of atoms in any normal object, you would have to wait far longer than the lifetime of the universe for tunneling to occur.*

SCHRÖDINGER'S EQUATION
Page 34
SUPERLUMINAL EXPERIMENTS
Page 78
THE JOSEPHSON JUNCTION
Page 132

Barrier

Classic behavior

Quantum behavior

SUPERLUMINAL EXPERIMENTS

THE MAIN CONCEPT | One consequence of quantum tunneling is the ability—in a small way—to be able to break the generally accepted speed limit for information. Ever since Albert Einstein introduced the special theory of relativity, this speed limit has been the speed of light. In its simplest form, a superluminal experiment consists of a beam of light and a barrier that photons can tunnel through. As tunneling happens instantaneously, photons that tunnel will cover the total distance in the time they took to cover the section of the experiment outside the barrier. This results in a total speed that is faster than the speed of light. For example, imagine a simple setup where a photon covers one unit of distance ordinarily, then the same distance again tunneling through a barrier. It will take the amount of time that light takes to cover one unit of distance to cover a total of two units—so it traveled at twice the speed of light. There remains a dispute between physicists over whether the photons can truly be considered to break the light speed barrier, or whether the signal is distorted by the process, a little like a runner leaning forward to break the tape first and hence appearing to complete the distance of the run quicker.

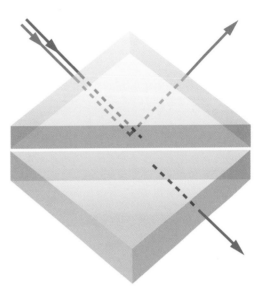

DRILL-DOWN | A kind of tunneling barrier that was discovered by Isaac Newton, known as frustrated total internal reflection, is often used by Austrian physicist and leading superluminal experimenter Günter Nimtz. When a beam of light enters a prism at a suitable angle, it bounces off the back of the glass rather than passing out of the prism, a process called total internal reflection. But Newton discovered that a second prism, placed close to but not touching the first, would enable part of the beam to flow through to the new prism instead of reflecting back. This happens because the photons tunnel through the barrier formed by the gap between the prisms.

SCHRÖDINGER'S EQUATION
Page 34
WINDOWS & BEAM SPLITTERS
Page 74
TUNNELING
Page 76

MATTER | *Mozart's Fortieth Symphony has been transmitted at four times the speed of light. Physicists originally suggested that, while superluminal experiments apparently broke the speed of light barrier, they could only do so for random photons—the effect couldn't be used to transmit ordered information. In 1995, Nimtz demonstrated that it could, by sending a Mozart recording through a superluminal setup.*

"Quantum mechanics is certainly imposing. But an inner voice tells me that it is not yet the real thing . . . I, at any rate, am convinced that He is not playing at dice."

ALBERT EINSTEIN
LETTER OF EINSTEIN TO MAX BORN, 1926

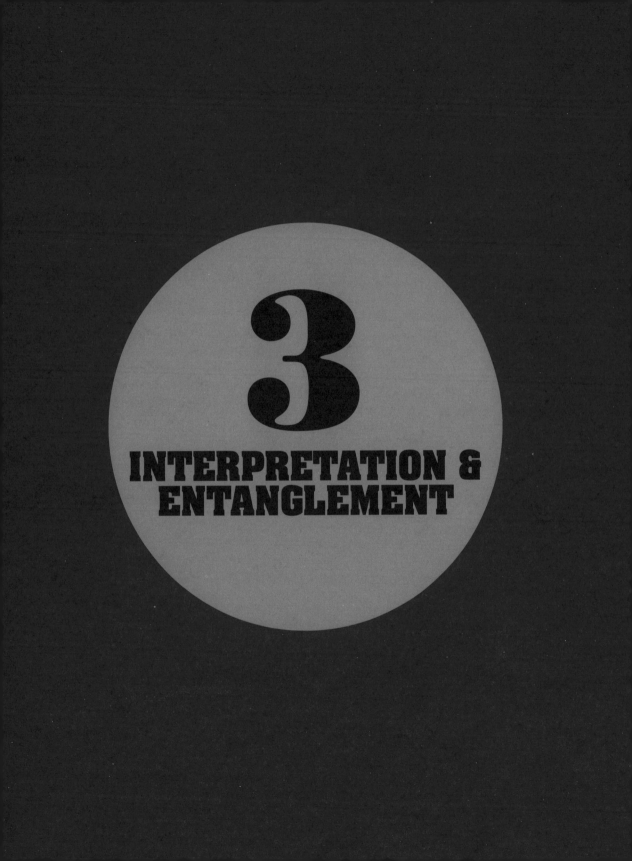

3
INTERPRETATION &
ENTANGLEMENT

INTERPRETATION GAME

Quantum physics is known for its "interpretations" such as the Copenhagen interpretation. These are attempts to provide an interface between the mathematical formalities of quantum theory and observation. No other branch of science feels the need for interpretations. No one provides interpretations for, say, evolutionary theory or the periodic table. Note that this is not merely explaining a complex theory in a way that is widely comprehensible. Popular science does this all the time. The interpretations of quantum physics are different beasts indeed.

The interpretations are not for communication to the public—they are designed for quantum physicists themselves. These theoretical approaches act as bridges between the mathematical structures of quantum physics and the practical observations made in experiments and everyday life. They seem to be required because of the surprisingly ad hoc nature of the development of quantum theory.

Theoretical leaps

Anyone telling the story of quantum theory tends to go straight from Albert Einstein's assumption that photons were real to Niels Bohr's theory of the quantum atom to Erwin Schrödinger and Werner Heisenberg developing mathematical representations of quantum systems, plus Max Born's explanation of Schrödinger's equation as representing the probability of finding a particle in a particular location.

What isn't obvious in this story is how much the theoreticians were making things up as they went along. All the experimental evidence pointed to light being wave-like. Einstein's assumption that particles of light (photons) were real entities went against every piece of experimental evidence, except for the photoelectric effect. It's as if someone assumed popcorn is alive because, despite all the evidence to the contrary, it does one thing—jumping around when heated—that living things also do.

Then we come to Bohr's atomic structure. It was at least partly inspired by New Zealand physicist Ernest Rutherford's discovery of the atomic nucleus in 1911, and the need to put electrons in a stable configuration. There was a degree of experimental evidence that went into it. Even so, Bohr went out on a limb by postulating his strange "electrons on rails" that could not spiral into the nucleus. It was only when he discovered Johann Balmer's work on the spectrum of hydrogen that there seemed to be some justification for making that leap.

As for Schrödinger, Heisenberg, and Born, there was no experimental starting point that inspired the approaches they took. Schrödinger's wave equation and Heisenberg's matrix mechanics were mathematical formulations that produced results that matched well with what had already been observed and, crucially with the many experiments that would come later—but no one could say *why*. Similarly, Born's assertion on probability was not a result of anything that was observed, but rather a guess that made more sense than the original concept of predicting the locations of particles. Again, experimental evidence came later.

So quantum theory had a stack of mathematical procedures that matched observation well, but no reason for saying why they were appropriate. At the same time, quantum theory described quantum behavior that seemed strange—uncanny even—when set against the observable behavior of ordinary objects made up of quantum particles. How was it possible to get from "here"—a set of quantum behaviors predicted by the math—to "there"—the behavior of, say, a tennis ball or a container of gas?

A philosophy of reality

What the constructors of the interpretations were doing was more philosophy than physics. It is no surprise, then, that a major player in the Copenhagen interpretation was Bohr—the most philosophical of quantum physicists. Not everyone appreciated this. The third-generation quantum physicist John Bell called Bohr "an obscurantist." Bohr's approach seems to have been driven by philosopher Immanuel Kant's realization that we can never know the reality of nature. All we can do is consider the phenomena we experience and use induction to suggest what lies beneath.

Bohr incorporated Kant's philosophy into an interpretation that made it clear that all we can do with quantum theory is predict the outcomes of measurements. In this interpretation, there is nothing we can ever know lying behind these measurements. Before we measure a particle's location, for example, it's not that we don't know its location. It doesn't have one. Other interpretations attempted to make Bohr's bleak assessment more approachable, or to replace it with a reality beneath. Arguably, no interpretation is entirely satisfactory.

BIOGRAPHIES

DAVID BOHM (1917–1992)

Born in Pennsylvania, United States, in 1917, David Bohm worked with Robert Oppenheimer during World War II and contributed to the Manhattan Project, developing nuclear weapons. When increasing anti-communist feeling in the United States led to Bohm being required to testify against Oppenheimer in 1949, Bohm refused and was charged with contempt of Congress. Although acquitted, he lost his job and worked for a number of years in Brazil and Israel before settling in the UK in 1957. There, he became Professor of Theoretical Physics at Birkbeck College, London, and a British citizen. He had considered an alternative to the existing interpretation of quantum physics since the early 1950s—now he fully developed his radically different interpretation. Influenced both by Albert Einstein's concerns about the probabilistic aspects of quantum theory and the philosophy of Jiddu Krishnamurti, which stressed the oneness and connectedness of the universe, Bohm produced an interpretation of quantum physics where each particle is influenced by every other. Bohm's approach mixed conventional physics with a mystical philosophical approach. Bohm died in London, England, in 1992, aged 74.

JOHN BELL (1928–1990)

Born in Belfast, Northern Ireland, in 1928, John Stewart Bell came from a working-class background—his siblings all left school age fourteen. After gaining a physics degree from Queen's University Belfast, Bell went straight to work at the UK's atomic research establishment at Harwell. While at Harwell, he completed a PhD at the University of Birmingham, and in 1960 moved with his wife Mary (also a Harwell physicist) to the European CERN laboratory near Geneva, Switzerland. His day job involved particle physics, but a sabbatical in 1963 enabled him to engage in his definitive work on quantum physics. Bell had some sympathy with Albert Einstein's doubts. He once remarked: "I hesitated to think it might be wrong, but I knew that it was rotten." In 1935, Einstein had come up with a thought experiment that showed either there was a flaw in quantum physics, and the properties of particles did have actual values, or the concept of "local reality," that particles didn't influence each other at a distance, was untrue. Bell came up with a hypothetical test that would distinguish between these two possibilities. Later experimenters, using Bell's analysis, showed that quantum theory is not incorrect. Bell died in Geneva in 1990, aged sixty-two.

HUGH EVERETT (1930–1982)

Formally Hugh Everett III, this US physicist was born in Washington DC in 1930. He originally studied to be a chemical engineer, but moved via mathematics into physics. By now at Princeton, his PhD advisor was John Wheeler, previously Richard Feynman's advisor. Everett's PhD thesis expanded on a paper he had written entitled "Wave Mechanics Without Probability." His primary idea was that the concept of wave function collapse was not necessary. If, rather than looking at individual particles, all interactions were taken into account, the picture transformed from one of two probabilities being selected to both possibilities taking place. His approach became known as the "many worlds" interpretation because one way of looking at it is that each time there is a quantum event, the universe splits into two versions, one for each possible outcome. Everett went on to work in defense on nuclear weapons, first for the government and then in industry. This saw yet another move in his interest from physics to computers; he spent much of his later career on computer programming, particularly for statistical applications. Everett died in McLean, Virginia, in 1982, aged fifty-one.

ALAIN ASPECT (1947–)

French physicist Alain Aspect was born in Agen, in the Bordeaux region, in 1947. After gaining a physics doctorate in Paris, he spent three years from 1971 in Cameroon as an aid worker. In the evenings, he took the opportunity to think through the areas of physics that fascinated him, notably quantum theory. He had come across both Albert Einstein's EPR paper claiming quantum physics was flawed and John Bell's work, and took the opportunity of unchallenged thinking to devise an experiment that could settle the dispute over the nature of quantum physics once and for all. There had been some attempts in the United States to explore the effects of quantum entanglement, which lay at the heart of the uncertainty over quantum physics, but they were inconclusive. By the time Aspect returned to Paris, he had the experiment set up in his mind. Here, Aspect undertook the entanglement test that Bell had envisaged. The result was a triumph—establishing that entanglement really did break the concept of local reality. Although future experiments would produce more detail, Aspect got there first. At the time of writing, Aspect is still working in the quantum field, specializing in materials known as Bose-Einstein condensates.

TIMELINE

EPR PAPER
Albert Einstein, assisted by Boris Podolsky and Nathan Rosen, writes a paper suggesting quantum physics incorporates a serious flaw. This "EPR" paper concludes that either it is possible for quantum particles to instantly interact at any distance, or quantum theory is wrong. But the quantum entanglement mechanism behind this prediction proves real.

1927　　**1935**　　**1951**

QUANTUM BEHAVIOR
Niels Bohr and Werner Heisenberg finish developing their "Copenhagen interpretation" of quantum physics. Although never formally written down, this provides an explanation for quantum behavior in terms of probabilities and wave function collapse. Incorporating concepts such as wave/particle duality and complementarity, it remains the most widely supported interpretation.

BOHM INTERPRETATION
David Bohm starts work on his alternative interpretation of quantum physics based on pilot waves. Inspired by this idea of Louis de Broglie, Bohm takes a totally different view of reality, suggesting that it is impossible to separate a quantum system of particles from interaction with everything around it.

MULTIPLE UNIVERSES

Hugh Everett writes the paper "Wave Mechanics Without Probability," originating the "many worlds" interpretation of quantum physics. This moves away from the idea of wave function collapse and instead proposes that, effectively, all possible outcomes of quantum interactions occur, creating vast numbers of different universes.

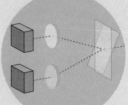

DATA ENCRYPTION

Chinese researchers led by Pan Jian-Wei first send entangled photons from the satellite Micius to ground stations on Earth over 750 miles (1,200 km) apart. This makes it practical to use quantum entanglement to provide unbreakable encryption between widespread locations, essential to providing a "quantum internet."

1956   **1964**   **2017**

ENTANGLED PARTICLES

John Bell writes his paper "On the Einstein–Podolsky–Rosen Paradox," establishing the Bell's inequality measure. This is a way to practically test whether or not entangled particles truly can interact instantly at any distance, or whether there are "hidden variables" that predetermine the outcome.

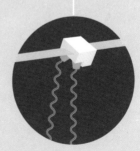

THE COPENHAGEN INTERPRETATION

THE MAIN CONCEPT | The behavior of quantum particles and systems is very different from what is observed in everyday objects made from those particles. By the late 1920s, Niels Bohr and Werner Heisenberg felt it necessary to answer the growing demand for an explanation that went beyond mathematical calculation. Their "Copenhagen interpretation" is arguably less of an explanation and more of a statement that there is nothing to explain. As it isn't a document, it's hard to be clear what makes up the Copenhagen interpretation. It certainly includes the idea that quantum systems don't have parameters with fixed values, only probabilities until observed. The act of observation invokes "wave function collapse," producing observed values. Rather than the separate concepts of waves and particles, the Copenhagen interpretation requires wave/particle duality and complementarity—the idea that a quantum object can behave as if it were a wave or a particle, but not both simultaneously. It incorporates the uncertainty principle. And it assumes it is possible to treat the laboratory and equipment in it as operating classically without quantum considerations. Opponents of the interpretation complain that it interprets what is observed without any attempt to reach an underlying reality. Supporters suggest that this is all that is possible, leading to the mantra "shut up and calculate."

DRILL-DOWN | A series of lectures given by Heisenberg in 1929 seem to have been the origin of the Copenhagen interpretation. In his book based on the lectures, *The Physical Principles of the Quantum Theory*, Heisenberg refers to the "Copenhagen spirit of quantum theory," referring to the approach developed at Bohr's Copenhagen-based institute. Bohr and Heisenberg never set out the interpretation in any detail, and would frequently contradict each other on minor details. The actual term "Copenhagen interpretation" seems to have been first used by Heisenberg in the 1950s, when alternative interpretations were being published and it seemed necessary to give this "Copenhagen spirit" a more technical-sounding title.

MATTER | *The Institute of Theoretical Physics in Copenhagen (now the Niels Bohr Institute) was founded by Bohr in 1921. It became the de facto European center for quantum physics in the 1920s and 1930s. The institute was largely funded by the Carlsberg brewery, which also provided Bohr with use of its "House of Honor," including an unlimited supply of free lager.*

WAVE/PARTICLE DUALITY
Page 30
PROBABILITY REIGNS
Page 54
COLLAPSING WAVE FUNCTIONS
Page 56

THE BOHM INTERPRETATION

THE MAIN CONCEPT | Not everyone was happy with Niels Bohr's Copenhagen interpretation of quantum behavior. In the 1920s, French physicist Louis de Broglie, who had developed the idea that particles such as electrons could act as waves, developed the pilot wave theory, where each particle had an associated wave that guided it. When the double-slit experiment was performed with particles, he said it was the pilot waves that went through both slits, causing interference. US–British physicist David Bohm picked this idea up in the 1950s and developed it to provide a full interpretation of quantum physics (it is often known as the de Broglie–Bohm theory). Unlike the Copenhagen interpretation, Bohm's version always has actual values for the positions of particles. However, each particle is constantly influenced by others around it—in principle, by every other particle in the universe—and this results in the observed quantum oddities. Initially, Bohm's work was not taken seriously, but although few support the full interpretation, it has come to be considered an interesting alternative. Bohm's theory takes a different approach to Max Born's idea that the mathematical square of the wave function gives us probabilities of finding a particle in a certain location. If Bohm's interpretation were true, Born's idea should not always be the case—but as yet, there is no experimental evidence supporting Bohm's interpretation.

DRILL-DOWN | Bohm's interpretation returns us to a deterministic universe— the clockwork universe that Newton's laws predicted. As French scholar Pierre-Simon Laplace observed at the end of the eighteenth century, in such a universe an entity that could access perfect information about every object in the universe could map out the entire future. However, the big difference from the Newtonian universe is that Bohm's is nonlocal—a particle on the far side of the universe could (and indeed would) influence a particle here, instantly. For many physicists, the lack of locality was a huge stumbling block because such a remote influence seemed impossible. However, quantum experiments involving entanglement do demonstrate nonlocal effects.

MATTER | *Late in his career, and related to his interpretation, Bohm came up with the concept of "implicate and explicate order." These are two different frameworks of reality, where the implicate order is where quantum phenomena takes place and is less dependent on time and space, more on connectedness, while the explicate order reflects what our perception of reality tells us.*

WAVE/PARTICLE DUALITY
Page 30
THE COPENHAGEN INTERPRETATION
Page 88
BELL'S INEQUALITY
Page 100

THE OBSERVER EFFECT

THE MAIN CONCEPT | In the early days of quantum physics, the concept of wave function collapse when a "measurement" was made caused confusion and drove some scientists to the extreme viewpoint that the involvement of conscious observers impacted on quantum systems. It was suggested that the act of being observed by a conscious observer caused wave function collapse. So, in the case of the Schrödinger's cat experiment, where we would now consider the measuring equipment monitoring the radioactive particle to be sufficient to cause decoherence and apparent collapse, the requirement for a conscious observer seemed to mean that the cat would indeed be both alive and dead until the box was opened and a conscious observer collapsed the wave function into one option. The (somewhat tenuous) argument behind the importance of the conscious observer is that they can see the world in only one particular state at a time, so they force collapse to occur. Hungarian–US physicist Eugene Wigner, probably the greatest supporter of such "consciousness collapse" of the wave function, suggested that if there was a variant of the Schrödinger's cat experiment where a human was in the box as well (with a gas mask), then there would be no superposition as the observer would be constantly collapsing the wave function.

DRILL-DOWN | If a conscious mind could influence a quantum system, could consciousness be a quantum phenomenon? This has been suggested by British physicist Roger Penrose, who proposes a link between the quantum wave function and the operations of the brain producing - consciousness. Many scientists are doubtful of Penrose's suggestion, which is not supported by any experimental evidence. Ironically, Penrose also proposes an alternative to the Copenhagen interpretation where wave function collapse is a real process, not caused by observers (and certainly not conscious observers), but by an interaction between a quantum system and gravity, where too big a difference in the space-time curvature of the superposed quantum states brings on a collapse.

MATTER | *Albert Einstein often discussed quantum theory with physicist Abraham Pais, who supported conventional quantum physics. In one conversation about Einstein's idea that there was something real and nonprobabilistic behind what we observe, Einstein asked Pais if he "really believed that the Moon exists only when I look at it." Einstein's comment underlines the unlikely nature of the observer effect.*

THE MANY WORLDS INTERPRETATION

THE MAIN CONCEPT | For physicists who do not accept the Copenhagen interpretation, where a collection of probabilities coalesce into distinct outcomes only when a quantum system interacts with another one, the "many worlds" interpretation provides a way out. Dreamed up by US physicist Hugh Everett and forming the basis of his PhD thesis, the many worlds approach totally removes the concept of wave function collapse. Instead, the suggestion is that we need to consider the total wave function covering the whole universe (or the part of it under observation). This never collapses, but each time a quantum system has the option of being in different states, all possible states actually occur. In effect (if not literally), the universe branches to incorporate one version of itself where, say, a particle is spin "up," and one version where the particle is spin "down." We cannot experience the whole many worlds universe because we inevitably take a single path through the universe where particular outcomes occur—but a different version of us could be said to experience each of the other possibilities. We no longer have the problem in a double-slit experiment of how a particle can appear to go through both slits—it goes through one slit in one set of the worlds and the other in a second set.

DRILL-DOWN | Those who believe that the many worlds hypothesis reflects reality argue that it should be possible to play quantum Russian roulette. If you fire a gun at your head, they argue, in some of the many worlds outcomes, the gun will not fire. As the only versions of you that will remain aware of the experience will be those where the gun failed, you will always find that you survive. Apart from the obvious risk that the theory is wrong, some suggest that because the many worlds interpretation allows us to experience only one path through the various quantum options, the chances are that the path the current conscious "you" inhabits will not provide a happy ending.

MATTER | *A natural reaction to the many worlds interpretation is that it falls foul of Occam's razor. Occam's razor is a simple mechanism for choosing between options where there is no evidence to support the choice, named for the fourteenth-century theologian William of Ockham. Although often now stated as making the choice with the fewest assumptions, the original "plurality must not be posited without necessity" seems particularly apt here.*

EINSTEIN'S OPPOSITION

THE MAIN CONCEPT | Albert Einstein was one of the founders of quantum physics, showing it was necessary for light to come in the form of photons to explain the photoelectric effect. However, as a fuller picture of quantum theory developed in the 1920s, he became increasingly uncomfortable with its probabilistic nature. According to Niels Bohr, until a quantum system was observed, it would evolve through time as a set of probabilities without any "real" value for, say, the location of a quantum particle. It was only when the system interacted with another—for instance, when a measurement was made—that an actual value existed. Einstein instinctively felt that this had to be wrong. He believed there was a solid reality underlying what happened. We might not be able to discover the value of a property before measurement, but it still had one—an approach known as "hidden variables." This requires that the value may be inaccessible, but it is still there in reality, unlike Bohr's set, or "cloud," of probabilities. Einstein began to challenge the accepted view, both by writing about his discomfort to his friend Max Born, who devised the probability aspect of quantum theory, and by challenging Niels Bohr with increasingly complex thought experiments that Einstein hoped would prove quantum theory wrong.

DRILL-DOWN | In his letters to Born, Einstein came up with some of his best-known remarks. These include: "I find the idea quite intolerable that an electron exposed to radiation should choose of its own free will, not only its moment to jump off but its direction. In that case, I would rather be a cobbler, or even an employee in a gaming house, than a physicist" and "[Quantum] theory says a lot, but does not really bring us any closer to the secret of the 'old one.'"

MATTER | *Einstein presented Bohr with his best counterargument to quantum theory over breakfast at a conference. The experiment, which involved the change in weight and time when a photon left a box, seemed to challenge the uncertainty principle. It took Bohr until the following day's breakfast to realize Einstein had forgotten to include the impact of general relativity, which wiped out the apparent paradox.*

PROBABILITY REIGNS
Page 54

THE COPENHAGEN INTERPRETATION
Page 88

THE EPR PAPER
Page 98

THE EPR PAPER

THE MAIN CONCEPT | In 1935, Albert Einstein along with Boris Podolsky and Nathan Rosen wrote a paper titled "Can Quantum-Mechanical Description of Physical Reality Be Considered Complete?", which is usually referred to by the initials of its authors, the "EPR" paper. The short work throws down a challenge to its readers. It shows that, if quantum physics is correct, then when two particles are produced in a state known as entanglement, observing a property such as the position or momentum of one particle instantly makes the other particle adopt a particular value for the equivalent property. But according to quantum theory, those properties are not established until the first particle is observed. Before then, all that exists is probability. The EPR paper suggests making measurements of both properties, then closes with a stark choice—either quantum theory is incorrect or entanglement makes it necessary to do away with a concept called local reality. The EPR paper comments: "No reasonable definition of reality could be expected to permit this." Local reality has two components. "Local" means that it shouldn't be possible to make something happen remotely without something traveling between the two locations. And "reality" means that particles should have properties such as location that have a real value, even if that value is not accessible.

DRILL-DOWN | The original EPR paper described measuring both the position and momentum of a pair of entangled particles. In each case, the measurement of the property for one particle has an implication for the measurement on the other particle. The use of both momentum and position caused considerable confusion, as some thought that the intention of the paper was to challenge Heisenberg's uncertainty principle, which relates momentum and position. Einstein wrote to Erwin Schrödinger that having the two properties *"ist mir Wurst,"* literally "is sausage to me"—meaning "I couldn't care less about it." Later versions of the EPR thought experiment avoided this confusion by using the single property of quantum spin.

MATTER | *According to the physicist and biographer Abraham Pais, when Niels Bohr first heard of the EPR paper and its apparent challenge to quantum theory, he burst into a colleague's room shouting "Podolsky, Opodolsky, Iopodolsky, Siopodolsky, Asiopodolsky, Basiopodolsky." His explanation that this was meant to be a parody of a line in Ludvig Holberg's play* Ulysses von Ithaca *did not particularly help.*

WAVE/PARTICLE DUALITY
Page 30
THE UNCERTAINTY PRINCIPLE
Page 38
EINSTEIN'S OPPOSITION
Page 96

BELL'S INEQUALITY

THE MAIN CONCEPT | The EPR paper described a thought experiment, but it was not a practical experiment to carry out. In 1964, Irish physicist John Bell, while on a sabbatical from his job at the CERN particle physics laboratory, thought up a measurement that would make it possible to distinguish between whether there were "hidden variables" and local reality was maintained, or the quantum physicists were right. Bell's sympathies were with Albert Einstein. He too was uncomfortable with some aspects of quantum theory, although he was less sure than Einstein they were wrong. He once said: "I felt that Einstein's intellectual superiority over [Niels] Bohr, in this instance, was enormous; a vast gulf between the man who saw clearly what was needed, and the obscurantist." Bell imagined producing a pair of entangled particles from a single original particle (one of the simplest ways to generate entanglement), then using detectors to check the spins a distance away from each other. These detectors would be randomly oriented at different angles to each other. He proved that, were this the case, a reality with hidden variables would not produce the kind of linked behavior predicted by quantum theory. This "Bell's inequality" would enable an experimenter to decide whether quantum theory was wrong or local reality was breached.

DRILL-DOWN | Turning Bell's idea into a working experiment took over ten years. US physicists Abner Shimony, Mike Horne, John Clauser, and Richard Holt did make a first attempt, but their results were inconclusive. The definitive demonstration of the long-range connection of entanglement (Einstein referred to it as "spooky action at a distance") was made in Paris by the young French physicist Alain Aspect. The cleverest part of his approach was a way of ensuring the particles couldn't communicate by conventional means. He did this by changing the direction of the measurement twenty-five million times a second, too fast for the information to reach the other particle in time to influence it.

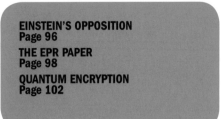

EINSTEIN'S OPPOSITION
Page 96

THE EPR PAPER
Page 98

QUANTUM ENCRYPTION
Page 102

MATTER | *Bell used the example of physicist Reinhold Bertlmann's socks to illustrate how hidden variables could give the impression of communication at a distance. Bertlmann always wore odd socks. If you saw one of his feet and it had a green sock on, you instantly knew the other sock wasn't green, even if light hadn't had time to reach you from the other foot.*

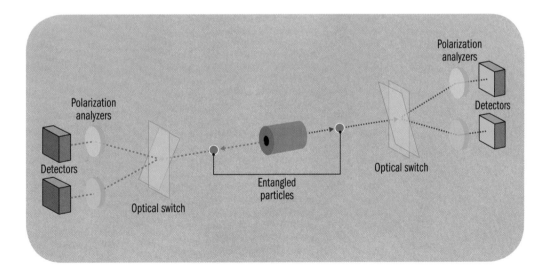

QUANTUM ENCRYPTION

THE MAIN CONCEPT | Throughout history, people have tried to keep messages secure. Since the early twentieth century, the unbreakable "one-time pad" method has been available. However, this relies on getting a key to both sender and receiver—a key that can be intercepted. What's more, unless the key is random, there's a chance it can be cracked. It was realized early on that the probabilistic nature of quantum physics means that a quantum source generates true random values—but it's still necessary to get the key to both sender and receiver. Quantum entanglement provides a way both to generate a random key and to get that key to the receiver and sender before it's generated. A stream of entangled particles is produced; each pair is split, one to the sender and one to the receiver. At this point, the key doesn't exist. If the sender examines the spin of the particles, the equivalent receiver's particles immediately adopt the opposite spin. The sequence of up or down spin is unpredictable, but the sender and receiver each get mirror-image versions of the key. The mechanism of quantum entanglement allows only random data to be sent, making it ideal to encrypt a conventional message, but it's impossible to use the entangled particles themselves as a communication channel.

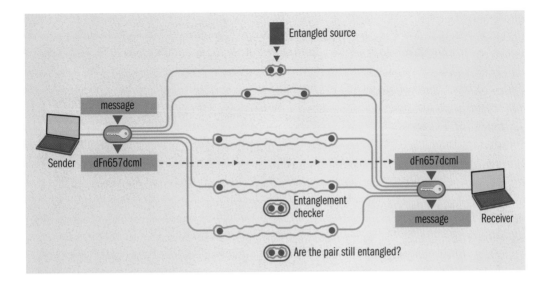

Entangled source

message

Sender dFn657dcml - - - - - - - > dFn657dcml

Entanglement checker

message Receiver

Are the pair still entangled?

DRILL-DOWN | It is possible to intercept entanglement-based quantum encryption. If someone captures one of the entangled stream of particles, they can read the values, then pass them onto their destination, leaving the particles in the form of the key. However, there is a way to test if pairs of particles are entangled. This takes a little longer, as an extra message has to be sent between receiver and sender, but is perfectly feasible. Any entanglement-based system has to regularly test the stream of particles, sampling every few particles to ensure that they still remain entangled. As long as the stream is known to be entangled, the communication link remains unbroken and secure.

MATTER | *Encryption using quantum entanglement was first demonstrated in Vienna, Austria in 2004, by sending a quantum encrypted request to transfer 3,000 euros from City Hall to Bank of Austria in nearby Schottengasse. Setting up the link over a distance of 0.3 miles (500 m) involved threading optical cables through Vienna's ancient sewers, previously best known as a setting for the Orson Welles movie* The Third Man.

PROBABILITY REIGNS
Page 54
THE EPR PAPER
Page 98
ENTANGLED SATELLITES
Page 106

QUANTUM TELEPORTATION

THE MAIN CONCEPT | As well as providing unbreakable encryption, quantum entanglement has another trick up its sleeve—teleportation. In effect, this is a small-scale version of the *Star Trek* transporter. Some time before entanglement became practical, the "no cloning" theorem was proved. This shows that it's impossible to make an exact copy of a quantum particle—the very act of discovering its properties changes them. However, with entanglement, something almost as good is possible. The process starts by providing both sender and receiver with one of a pair of entangled particles. The entangled particle is then used to interact with the particle to be teleported. Data from this interaction is sent by conventional communications to the receiver. The receiver then takes another particle of the same kind as the one to be teleported. This particle too undergoes a process along with the second entangled particle—the process is selected based on the conventional information transmitted. At the end of the process, one or more of the quantum properties will have been transferred from the sender's particle to the receiver's particle. The receiver's particle becomes the same as the sender's—in effect, it has been teleported. The process gets around the no-cloning theorem because the properties are never discovered— they are merely transferred by the entangled pair.

DRILL-DOWN | Because of the *Star Trek* transporter, an immediate response to the idea of quantum teleportation is that this is a way to make the transporter a reality. However, there are three issues. First is the difficulty of examining the atoms in an object and then reconstructing the object from its component atoms. Then there is the timescale involved. There are so many atoms in a human, for example—around 7,000 trillion trillion— it would take thousands of years to scan them. Finally, it is worth remembering that with teleportation, you are not transmitted. Your body would be destroyed while an identical version is created—not a pleasant thought.

MATTER | *Teleportation was first realized in 1997 by two teams in Europe: one under Anton Zeilinger (arguably Europe's leading quantum entanglement experimenter) in Vienna, Austria, and the other led by Francesco de Martini in Rome, Italy. The original experiment was not a complete teleportation of all properties, but transferred the polarization of one photon to another.*

ENTANGLED SATELLITES

THE MAIN CONCEPT | Whether your intention is encryption or teleportation, making use of entanglement requires a pair of entangled particles to be split, with one dispatched to each of sender and receiver. This is not trivial, because it's easy for quantum particles to interact with the environment and lose their entanglement. The original entanglement experiments involved short distances in the laboratory, but two key individuals have driven experiments that have led to greater distances. In Vienna, Austria Anton Zeilinger was the first to start the long-distance trials, sending entangled particles 0.4 miles (600 m) in 2003. The next year, Pan Jian-Wei, in Heifei, China, achieved 8 miles (13 km), shortly before Zeilinger extended his range to 9.5 miles (15.2 km). These distances were selected because through sea-level atmosphere, they are roughly equivalent to the much greater distance to a satellite through increasingly thinning atmosphere. The goal of using a satellite was achieved by Pan in 2017. This makes it possible to send the two halves of an entangled pair to base stations 870 miles (1,400 km) apart. Such satellites are likely to form the backbone of a "quantum internet," which would enable entangled communication to provide secure encrypted communication, or distributed quantum computing. Such a network would also require conventional connections, but we are likely to see many more entanglement generators on satellites.

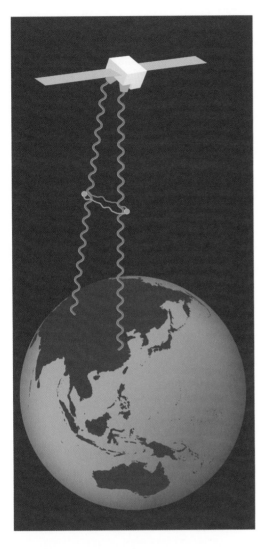

DRILL-DOWN | Ironically, one of the reasons we are likely to need a quantum entangled add-on to the internet is to keep our current internet connections secure from the attacks made possible by another quantum technology. Quantum computers, where each bit is a quantum particle, are far more powerful than conventional computers at certain processes. One of these is the ability to deduce the factors of a number produced by multiplying two very large prime numbers. Unfortunately, this is exactly the ability that is used in the RSA encryption used when a secure link is formed in the web (represented by a padlock in the browser). Quantum encryption may prove the only defense.

MATTER | *The intention had been to provide the first quantum entangled particles from space via the International Space Station in 2014, but this experiment never materialized. Instead, the Micius satellite, named for the Latinized name of fifth-century BCE philosopher Mozi (or Mo Tzu), was launched in August 2016, orbiting around 320 miles (500 km) above the Earth, and achieved first transmission less than a year later.*

QUBITS

THE MAIN CONCEPT | Current computers are reaching their physical limits in terms of power, but many labs are working on a new generation of technology—quantum computers. To appreciate these devices needs an understanding of their fundamental unit, the "qubit." A conventional computer uses bits, a contraction of "binary digit." These are simply stores that hold an electrical charge. If a bit has a low charge, it is given the value 0—if it holds a higher charge, it becomes 1. This means a bit can be used to hold data in binary form— numbers to base two—and is employed in all current computers. A qubit—a quantum bit—stores data as a property of a quantum particle, typically its spin. When measured, spin will always come out "up" or "down" in the direction of measurement, but before measurement, it holds both values in superposition, with a specific probability of having one or other value. Probabilities can be 50/50, but can also be any other split such as 35.1117/64.8883. Multiple qubits can be considered as a system with more combined values than the equivalent bits. For example, three bits can hold eight values: 000, 001, 100, 101, 010, 011, 110, and 111. But three qubits can have 256 possible values.

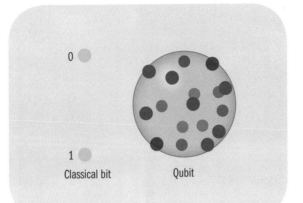

0 Classical bit
1

Qubit

DRILL-DOWN | A wide range of options is being considered to implement qubits. In principle, any quantum particle could act as a qubit, but the most frequently used are photons and electrons. Electrons have the advantage of being easy to manipulate, but are more likely to interact with each other, so require more sophisticated traps. Photons are harder to handle, but ignore each other. Most early qubits came in forms suitable only for laboratories, often involving special cavities and devices that needed cooling to cryogenic temperatures. However, some success has now been made in producing solid-state qubits, which make it far more possible that a device based on them could become mainstream.

QUANTUM SPIN
Page 44

DECOHERENCE
Page 58

QUANTUM COMPUTING
Page 110

MATTER | *The word "qubit," which appears to be inspired by the ancient unit of measurement the cubit (based on the distance from elbow to fingertip), first appeared in the 1995 paper "Quantum Coding" by Benjamin Schumacher. In his acknowledgments, Schumacher says: "The term 'qubit' was coined in jest in one of the author's many intriguing and valuable conversations with W. K. Wootters."*

QUANTUM COMPUTING

THE MAIN CONCEPT | As it has become practical to produce qubits—isolated quantum particles, using one of their quantum parameters as the equivalent of a bit—there has been furious activity attempting to make a working quantum computer. This would involve having sufficient qubits to produce effective calculation. Although modern conventional computers work on billions of bits at a time, because of the extra information involved in each qubit and the way they interact, it would be necessary to have only a few hundred or thousand qubits in a usable quantum computer. Because of the difficulties of protecting the qubits from decoherence and of getting data into, around, and out of a quantum computer, which uses entanglement, even such small numbers have proved immensely difficult. At the time of writing, IBM's fifty-qubit machine is the best to be achieved. However, hundreds of labs are working on different approaches to quantum computing. Because keeping qubits from decoherence usually needs extremely low temperatures or specialist environments, quantum computers as currently envisaged are the equivalent of the original vacuum-tube-based electronic computers: unwieldy and suitable only for one-off construction. However, it may prove possible to put some quantum computing functions in variants of conventional electronic chips, making a widely available computer with quantum facilities a longer-term possibility.

DRILL-DOWN | If a fully functional quantum computer were produced, we already have some algorithms to make them work, performing tasks that would take too long to complete on conventional computers. The earliest was Shor's algorithm, developed by Peter Shor in 1994. This makes it possible to find integers multiplied together to form a larger number extremely quickly, putting the widely used RSA encryption method at risk. Another algorithm of great interest to search companies is Grover's search algorithm, devised in 1996. Imagine you are searching one million locations for a particular piece of information. On average, a conventional search would require 500,000 tries. Grover's algorithm would get there in just 1,000.

MATTER | *A Canadian company, D-Wave, already sells a room-size quantum computer. However, this makes use of a specific process known as adiabatic quantum annealing. Instead of having logic gates like a conventional quantum computer, this makes use of a kind of analog quantum process. It has real benefits on certain applications such as image recognition, but isn't a general-purpose quantum computer.*

DECOHERENCE
Page 58

QUANTUM TELEPORTATION
Page 104

QUBITS
Page 108

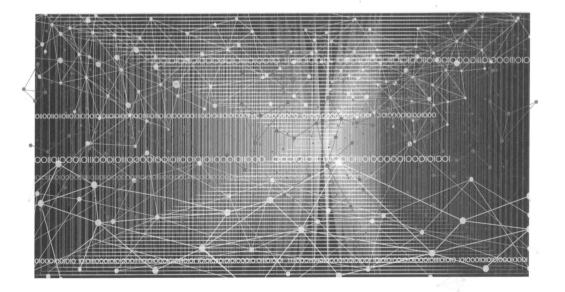

QUANTUM ZENO EFFECT

THE MAIN CONCEPT | One of the stranger effects associated with entanglement is the quantum Zeno effect. The "Zeno" part refers to ancient Greek philosopher Zeno, a student of Parmenides in the Eleatic school in the fifth century BCE. The school argued that all change was illusory, and Zeno came up with a series of paradoxes, attempting to demonstrate that there was something wrong with our understanding of movement and change. The quantum Zeno effect is supposedly based on Zeno's arrow—in fact, it would have been better to have called it the quantum watched-pot effect. As we have seen, the properties of a quantum particle take on a fixed value only when measured and are otherwise in superpositions of values. The quantum Zeno effect involves making repeated interactions with a quantum particle, as a result of which the property never moves away from a fixed value, rather like the proverbial watched pot. Although there are few practical applications of the quantum Zeno effect as yet, it has been suggested that it may play a role in the ability of some birds to navigate using the Earth's magnetic field. The suggested mechanism involves entanglement of electrons in the birds' eyes and may use the Zeno effect to avoid other interactions of the electrons.

DRILL-DOWN | Zeno's arrow is a paradox exploring the nature of motion. Imagine an arrow flying through space. Let's examine it at a moment in time; for comparison, let's put alongside it another arrow that is not moving. How can we tell the difference between the two? In that moment, each sits at a fixed location in space. And this is true for every moment of time. Which means that the arrow is not moving. There are two issues here: one is that the two arrows are not identical—one has kinetic energy, for example. The other issue is that an infinite set of infinitesimally small values can sum to a nonzero total.

MATTER | *Elea, the location of Parmenides' school, now known as Velia, was on the west coast of Italy. The rejection of motion and change seems counterintuitive; it was based on the idea that the universe had an underlying unchanging unity that we cannot directly experience through our senses. None of Zeno's writings survive, but we know of nine of his paradoxes via later writers.*

PROBABILITY REIGNS
Page 54

COLLAPSING WAVE FUNCTIONS
Page 56

THE EPR PAPER
Page 98

"But, but, but . . . if anyone says he can think about quantum theory without getting giddy, it merely shows that he hasn't understood the first thing about it!"

NIELS BOHR

4

THE AMAZING QUANTUM

THE QUANTUM REVOLUTION

We have seen how the shift from the nineteenth century to the twentieth involved a fundamental transformation in physics. At the same time, there was a significant change in the technological basis of industry and society. In the nineteenth century, the prime mover had been steam. The steam engine transformed both working life and, through the railways, transport. In the twentieth century, it was electricity and then electronics that took over in the transformative role.

Electrical lighting, then electric motors, began to make a huge difference to everyday life. As the use of electricity became commonplace, it increasingly took over communications too. First the telegraph and then radio shrank the world. It is not entirely surprising that when Albert Einstein first had his ideas on special relativity, dependent on an understanding of what simultaneity meant across different locations, he was working in the Swiss Patent Office in Bern, regularly handling patents for methods of using electricity to synchronize remote clocks.

The electronic age

With these more sophisticated uses of electricity came the need to produce more complex circuits. Crude devices that had been used to examine the behavior of an electrical phenomenon called "cathode rays" were transformed into versatile electrical devices known as vacuum tubes. These electrical components could force currents to flow in only one direction, could act as switches for the flow of electricity, or could amplify a small variation in an electrical signal so that, for example, a low-energy radio signal could be transformed into a sound loud enough to fill a room. With a better understanding of the electron's role in electrical currents, equipment making use of vacuum tubes became known as electronics.

At this stage, quantum theory was in its infancy. The first triode vacuum tubes, providing the switching and amplifying capabilities, became available around the same time as Bohr's quantum atom paper was published. Although electrons were beginning to be seen as quantum particles, it wouldn't be until the full-scale quantum revolution of Werner Heisenberg, Erwin Schrödinger, Max Born, and Paul Dirac that it was realized that the behavior of these quantum particles could be controlled more effectively using devices that were explicitly designed to make use of quantum behavior.

There was every need for such a device, because vacuum tubes were problematic. It's notable that when science-fiction writer James Blish conceived in the 1940s a probe that could enter the atmosphere of Jupiter, he noted that such probes couldn't have electronics on board as the atmospheric pressure would cause the fragile glass tubes to implode. Even in a more earthbound location, vacuum tubes were large, generated a lot of heat, and required high-voltage electricity, which itself needed heavy equipment to produce, meaning that electronic devices were not portable. Enter the transistor.

Although an early solid-state triode had been proposed back in 1926 by Julius Lilienfeld (whose patents caused problems for the team building transistors), it could not be made to work, in part because of a lack of understanding of the quantum nature of semiconductors—substances that sit between a conductor and an insulator, such as silicon and germanium—which would prove essential for the development of solid-state electronics.

Quantum proliferation

The reason a team from Bell Labs succeeded in getting the transistor operational in 1947 was that they were among the first electronic experts to have a firm grasp of quantum physics. It was this quantum expertise that became the driving force behind electronics, branching out into integrated circuits, lasers, LEDs (light-emitting diodes), and more. Explicit quantum devices such as these are now responsible for thirty-five percent of GDP in developed countries. Although this is a broad-brush figure, it seems a reasonable estimate given the importance of electronics in modern society. And this figure does not include the many occupations where the quantum revolution has transformed jobs. There were science writers, for example, before electronics—but jobs like this are now entirely dependent on computers, the internet, smartphones, and more.

Quantum physics is fascinating and gives a unique insight into the lowest-level workings of reality we can access, even if it emphasizes that this level tells us only about what we can measure rather than the true "reality" beneath. However, unlike much theoretical physics, quantum theory has also had a transforming impact on our everyday lives.

BIOGRAPHIES

HEIKE KAMERLINGH ONNES (1853–1926)

Born in Groningen, Netherlands, in 1853, Heike Kamerlingh Onnes was a master of the supercold. After attending university at Groningen and Heidelberg, he became professor of experimental physics at the University of Leiden in 1882, staying until 1923. There, he worked on low-temperature physics. His first big success was in 1908, when he managed to liquefy helium, getting the element down to a temperature of -456.97°F (-271.65°C), just 1.5 degrees above absolute zero (-459.67°F/-273.15°C), the lowest temperature that had ever been achieved. In 1911, working on the effects of low temperature on conductivity, he discovered that mercury went through a change of state at -452.11°F (-268.95°C), where its electrical resistance entirely disappeared—he had discovered the phenomenon of superconductivity. Kamerlingh Onnes was considered old-fashioned and overbearing (despite having many assistants, only his name tends to appear on his papers), but there is no doubt of his achievements. At the time, superconductivity was considered a useless oddity—when Kamerlingh Onnes won the Nobel Prize in 1913, the citation did not mention it—but it has come to be a significant application of quantum physics. He died in Leiden in 1926.

WILLIAM SHOCKLEY (1910–1989)

Born in London, England, in 1910 to US parents, physicist William Shockley was brought up in Palo Alto, California, and studied at Caltech and MIT. He went straight from his doctorate to Bell Labs, where he stayed until 1956, when he left to set up his own company, Shockley Semiconductor Laboratory, the first in Silicon Valley. After wartime work on radar, Shockley was asked to head up a team investigating solid-state physics with the hope of moving away from the delicate vacuum tubes used in early electronics. Shockley worked closely with John Bardeen and Walter Brattain, developing a solid-state equivalent of the triode, which they named the transistor. That this was a team effort was reflected in the three sharing the Nobel Prize in Physics in 1956. However, Shockley devised several of the theoretical advances that made transistors feasible, and invented two key types of transistor. Shockley was difficult to work with, alienating the other Bell team members and many of the staff at Shockley Semiconductor Laboratory. Eight of his staff split off to form their own, more successful company in 1957. In 1963, Shockley moved to Stanford University, where he worked until retirement. He died at Stanford in 1989.

THEODORE MAIMAN (1927–2007)

US engineer and physicist Theodore Maiman, born in Los Angeles in 1927, won the race to produce the first working laser. He had the ideal background: with a first degree from the University of Colorado in Engineering Physics, Maiman went on to get a Master's in Electrical Engineering and a PhD in Physics at Stanford. This combination of the practical engineering and the solid physics enabled him to overcome significant technical hurdles in producing a laser. Maiman, who had joined Hughes Corporation in 1956, had experience working with rubies in masers, the microwave equivalent of a laser. It was thought at the time, due to an erroneous report, that rubies wouldn't work in lasers, but Maiman was determined to give them a try. Inspired by the flashtube of an early electronic flash, he got his laser working on May 16, 1960. He was horrified when the press described his technology, intended to enhance communications, as a "science-fiction death ray." Maiman went on to head up a company specializing in lasers and another company that developed large-screen laser video displays. Despite being the first to produce a working laser, Maiman was excluded from the Nobel Prize. He died in Vancouver.

BRIAN JOSEPHSON (1940–)

Born in Cardiff, Wales, in 1940, apart from a short period as an assistant professor at the University of Illinois, Brian Josephson has spent his career at the University of Cambridge, England. Just two years after gaining his BA in Natural Sciences in 1962, Josephson wrote a paper called "Possible New Effects in Superconductive Tunnelling," on what became known as the "Josephson effect"—a tunneling mechanism in superconducting metal junctions. He won the 1973 Nobel Prize in Physics for this work. This joined a handful of known examples of quantum effects that could be directly used in a working device, proving particularly useful in components known as SQUIDs (superconducting quantum interference devices). Josephson was only thirty-three when he received the Nobel Prize. Toward the end of the 1970s, he became uncomfortable with the way science ignored areas of apparent experience such as telepathy and the paranormal. While still in the physics department, he set up his Mind–Matter Unification Project. It is arguable that Josephson has not contributed much to physics since his early work, but there is no doubt of his essential involvement in the development of quantum technology. He retired his professorship in 2007, but continues his research at Cambridge.

TIMELINE

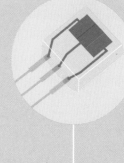

ELECTRON MICROSCOPE
The first electron microscope is constructed by Ernst Ruska and Max Knoll, beginning the move away from the dominance of optical instruments. Dependent on the discovery that electrons could behave as waves with much smaller wavelength than light, the device could resolve far smaller objects than a conventional microscope was able to.

1911 — **1931** — **1947**

SUPERCONDUCTIVITY
Just three years after becoming the first to achieve such low temperatures, Heike Kamerlingh Onnes discovers superconductivity in mercury at little over four degrees above absolute zero (-459.67°F/-273.15°C). At this temperature (-452.11°F/-268.95°C), the electrical resistance of the metal suddenly and unexpectedly drops to zero.

ELECTRONIC DEVICES
John Bardeen, Walter Brattain, and William Shockley demonstrate the transistor, the first step in solid-state electronics that would have been impossible to design without a knowledge of quantum physics. The transistor rapidly replaced vacuum-tube electronics and paved the way for all our modern electronic devices.

LASER LIGHT

Despite being told by experts that his design would not work, Theodore Maiman produces the first working laser at Hughes Corporation, using an artificial ruby. Based on a theory by Albert Einstein from over thirty years earlier, Maiman's laser produces "coherent" light, generating photons of very similar energy with their phases in step.

NUCLEAR FORCE

Quantum chromodynamics, an equivalent of quantum electrodynamics (QED) for the strong nuclear force between quarks, is developed. Because, unlike electrical charge, there are three different types of charge in the strong nuclear force (given the names "red," "blue," and "green"), the interaction of quarks and gluons (their equivalent of photons) is significantly more complex than QED.

1960   **1962**   **1973**

JOSEPHSON EFFECT

Twenty-two-year-old Brian Josephson discovers the "Josephson effect," leading to the development of Josephson junctions, single-electron transistors, and SQUIDs (superconducting quantum interference devices). Based on quantum tunneling in superconducting junctions, SQUIDs are ultrasensitive magnetic-field detectors with the potential to detect anything from variations in the Earth's field to unexploded bombs.

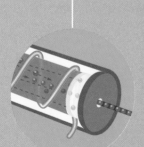

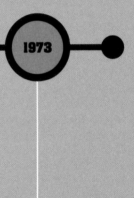

THE LASER

THE MAIN CONCEPT | Many of the experimental developments in quantum physics have been dependent on one quantum device: the laser. In the mid-1950s, the theory of the maser, standing for "microwave amplification through the stimulated emission of radiation," was developed by Russian physicists Alexander Prokhorov and Nikolai Basov, with a working maser produced by the US physicist Charles Townes soon after. This used a quantum interaction between photons and atoms in a material to amplify a microwave beam. Although masers could be used in telecommunications and atomic clocks, they were limited in power, and better alternatives could perform the same functions. It was clear that a version working with visible light would have much wider application. On May 16, 1960, US engineer and physicist Theodore Maiman constructed the first working laser, based on an artificial ruby and the tube from a camera flashgun. The key to the laser's effectiveness was that the stimulated emission process meant it had a single, sharp frequency and the phase of all the photons were in step—it was "coherent" light. This meant that a laser beam dispersed far less than ordinary light, making it ideal for telecommunications and as a specialist cutting device. Since 1960, a wide range of laser technologies has been developed, making the technology pervasive.

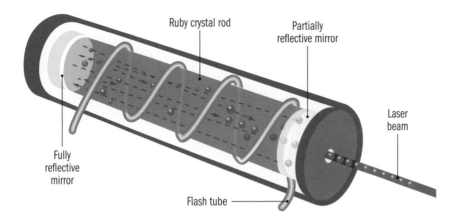

Ruby crystal rod

Partially
reflective mirror

Laser
beam

Fully
reflective
mirror

Flash tube

DRILL-DOWN | Most early lasers such as Maiman's were based on a ruby. Within a few years, these were joined by gas-based lasers, using less corrosive materials than the original experimental alkali metal gases. However, the real breakthrough in the modern ubiquity of the laser was the semiconductor device. Practically every domestic laser, whether in a CD, DVD, or Blu-ray player, laser printer, or laser pointer, is likely to be a semiconductor laser. These are tiny devices small enough to fit through the eye of a needle and operate on a similar principle to the light-emitting diode (LED), pumping electrons into a semiconductor, where they drop in energy to give off photons.

MATTER | *Despite Albert Einstein's opposition to the probabilistic aspects of quantum theory, the laser is another of his contributions to the quantum world. In 1917, based on Niels Bohr's idea of the quantum atom, Einstein suggested it would be possible for an atom to absorb a photon of light then release it in "stimulated emission" when a second photon hit the atom.*

THE QUANTUM ATOM
Page 28

THE PAULI EXCLUSION PRINCIPLE
Page 40

SUPERLUMINAL EXPERIMENTS
Page 78

THE TRANSISTOR

THE MAIN CONCEPT | In the early development of electronics, a particularly useful device called a triode was produced. This enabled a small electrical signal either to be amplified or to be used to switch another electrical current on and off. The amplification aspect was particularly useful in audio and broadcasting, while the switching ability made it possible to construct the logic gates that make an electronic computer possible. However, triode valves (vacuum tubes) were too large, fragile, and energy-consuming to be used in the large numbers required by most electronic devices—and impractical for anything portable. The transistor was devised as a solid-state replacement for the triode: small, robust, and low in energy consumption. Its design depended fundamentally on an understanding of quantum physics. The simplest form of transistor was a sandwich of three slices of a semiconductor such as silicon or germanium. These were produced in two forms, "n-type" (typically "doped" by adding a small amount of phosphorus) and "p-type" (typically doped with boron). The n-type semiconductor has extra electrons, whereas the p-type has fewer than usual. The sandwich would be set up in either n-p-n or p-n-p format, with the central slice controlling the electrical current flowing between the other two. The transistor, particularly when built into integrated circuits, transformed electronics.

DRILL-DOWN | A modern computer processor can contain 500 million transistors. Cramming these in requires "integrated circuits," where all the components are formed as layers on the surface of a silicon chip. Here, the transistors are typically MOSFET ("metal oxide semiconductor field effect transistor"). The field effect transistor was devised before the first working transistors, but was initially impractical to construct. Instead of using a central "slice" of semiconductor, it has an external electrode called a gate, which sits over a gap between two pieces of semiconductor and uses an electrical field to control the current. Other forms of transistor used in flash memory make use of tunneling effects to store charge.

MATTER | *The first computer using transistors was built at the University of Manchester, England, in 1953, just six years after John Bardeen, William Shockley, and Walter Brattain made the original transistor. Up until then, electronic computers had been huge and impractical for many purposes—for example, the 1946 ENIAC had 20,000 vacuum tubes and needed 150 kilowatts of electricity to run.*

THE QUANTUM ATOM
Page 28

QUANTUM FIELD THEORY
Page 62

TUNNELING
Page 76

THE ELECTRON MICROSCOPE

THE MAIN CONCEPT | In 1924, just three years after French physicist Louis de Broglie suggested that electrons had wave-like behavior, this was experimentally demonstrated. By 1931, the concept found a practical application in microscopes that use electrons. Conventional microscopes use light and lenses to examine small objects. But the resolution of a microscope—the minimum scale at which it can focus—is limited by the wavelength of light. It is impossible to pick up detail that is much smaller than a single wavelength. A light-based microscope can resolve down to around 200 nanometers—0.2 millionths of a meter—providing approximately ×2,000 magnification. But the best electron microscopes can resolve down to around 50 picometers—0.05 billionths of a meter—providing magnification of up to ×10,000,000. As early as 1933, German physicist Ernst Ruska developed a prototype electron microscope with better resolution than was possible with light. The approach is a little like an upside-down optical microscope. Instead of light passing up through the sample to the lens, this type of electron microscope sends a focused beam of electrons through a thin sample, then focuses the result on a phosphorescent viewing screen or photographic plate below. Soon after, an alternative electron microscope was developed that uses the impact of electrons on the surface of a sample.

DRILL-DOWN | The earliest design of electron microscope is the "transmission electron microscope." However, by 1937, an alternative "scanning electron microscope" was developed, passing an electron beam over the sample and detecting the electrons or electromagnetic radiation generated from the surface by this bombardment. Both are still used. Scanning electron microscopes have lower resolution than transmission electron microscopes, but don't penetrate the surface of samples and so can deal with thicker or three-dimensional samples. There is, however, a limit to the kind of samples scanning electron microscopes can examine. Such samples need to be hard and dry to withstand a high vacuum and, if not electrically conducting, need a thin conductive coating added.

MATTER | *The scanning tunneling microscope is sometimes confused with an electron microscope, but is a different electron-based quantum device, developed in 1981. A scanning tunneling microscope uses a tiny conducting tip that rides over the surface of the sample, measuring the electrical current tunneling between the tip and the surface. This microscope can also manipulate matter down to the level of individual atoms.*

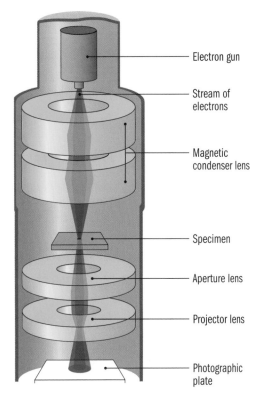

— Electron gun

— Stream of electrons

— Magnetic condenser lens

— Specimen

— Aperture lens

— Projector lens

— Photographic plate

WAVE/PARTICLE DUALITY
Page 30

QUANTUM DOUBLE SLIT
Page 42

TUNNELING
Page 76

SUPERCONDUCTORS

THE MAIN CONCEPT | One quantum peculiarity caused a major shock when discovered. Dutch physicist Heike Kamerlingh Onnes, working at the University of Leiden, was an expert on low temperatures. In 1911, he was studying the conductivity of metals near to absolute zero (-459.67°F/-273.15°C). As he lowered the temperature of mercury, it went through a sudden change at -452.11°F (-268.95°C), losing all electrical resistance. Usually the electrons flowing through an electrical conductor interact with the atoms, resulting in resistance. But once superconducting, electrons carried on as if there was nothing to stop them. To test the effect, Kamerlingh Onnes started an electrical current in a superconducting wire. He could keep the experiment going for only a few hours, but in that timescale, the flow continued unchecked. A more sophisticated experiment run in the 1950s continued for eighteen months with no detectable change in current. Kamerlingh Onnes immediately thought of the benefit for electricity distribution, where loss of energy to heat through electrical resistance is a significant problem. However, the need to keep superconductors at extremely low temperatures has limited their use to generating powerful magnetic fields in specialist equipment. Basic superconductivity (there are several types) was later explained as a quantum effect where electrons act together, unified by the influence of the superconductor.

DRILL-DOWN | The main drawback of superconductors is the need to keep them at extremely low temperatures. For decades, attempts have been made to find a material that was superconducting at higher temperatures—ideally requiring no special cooling. By the 1980s, superconductors based on special ceramic materials that combined, for example, mercury, barium, calcium, copper, and oxygen, were working in the range of -297.4°F (-183°C) to -234.4°F (-148°C). This is a significant improvement on the early superconductors, because such cooling can be produced with liquid nitrogen rather than the far more expensive and tricky to handle liquid helium. Experimenters continue to search for the elusive room-temperature superconducting material.

THE UNCERTAINTY PRINCIPLE
Page 38
THE MRI SCANNER
Page 130
THE JOSEPHSON JUNCTION
Page 132

MATTER | *As well as reducing electrical resistance to zero, a superconductor produces the so-called Meissner effect, named for German physicist Walther Meissner. The Meissner effect says that any magnetic field is expelled from a material as it becomes superconducting. This leads to a dramatic demonstration of superconductivity, as a magnet will levitate above a superconductor because its magnetic field is unable to penetrate the material.*

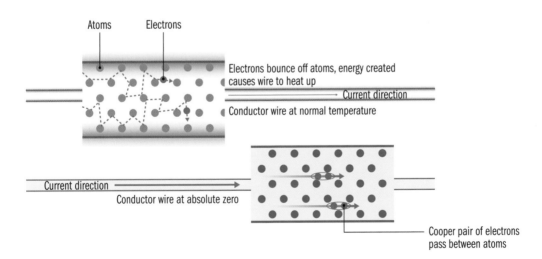

Atoms   Electrons

Electrons bounce off atoms, energy created causes wire to heat up

Current direction

Conductor wire at normal temperature

Current direction

Conductor wire at absolute zero

Cooper pair of electrons pass between atoms

THE MRI SCANNER

THE MAIN CONCEPT | The most sophisticated piece of quantum technology many of us encounter is the MRI scanner, incorporating multiple quantum devices. The initials "MRI" stand for "magnetic resonance imaging"—the name was changed from the more accurate NMR, "nuclear magnetic resonance," as the word "nuclear" was disconcerting. Rather than use hazardous X-rays, MRI scanners turns atoms into radio transmitters. The scanner works on the hydrogen in the human body's water molecules. As the body passes through the scanner, a strong magnetic field is applied. This flips the quantum spins of the protons in those hydrogen atoms. When the magnetic field is switched off, the spins flip back, producing radio-frequency photons. This electromagnetic radiation is picked up by receiver coils, building up a picture from the signals from these vast numbers of tiny transmitters. Such manipulation of spin is a quantum effect, but another is required to produce the magnetic field that triggers it. Scanners use extremely powerful magnets to provide the field required to flip spins. The magnets are cooled to very low temperatures, typically around -452°F (-269°C), using liquid helium. At this temperature, the magnets become superconductors, enabling unusually strong fields to be produced. Superconducting magnets have found use in a range of specialist applications that require intense magnetic fields.

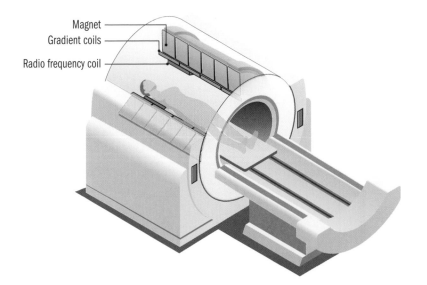

Magnet
Gradient coils
Radio frequency coil

DRILL-DOWN | Superconducting magnets are used whenever extremely strong magnetic fields are required. The most impressive use is in the largest machine in the world, the Large Hadron Collider (LHC) at the CERN laboratory near Geneva, Switzerland. In the LHC, around 10,000 superconducting magnets are used to keep the beams of protons that circulate around the accelerator on track. Elsewhere, superconducting magnets are being used in experimental Maglev trains, which float above the track and are accelerated along it by magnetic interaction. The first planned commercial Maglev train, the Chou Shinkansen, linking Tokyo, Nagoya, and Osaka in Japan, is expected to reach speeds of around 500 kilometers per hour (320 miles per hour).

QUANTUM SPIN
Page 44

QUANTUM ELECTRODYNAMICS
Page 66

SUPERCONDUCTORS
Page 128

MATTER | *MRI scanners are infamously noisy. This is because smaller electromagnets called gradient coils are turned on and off to make changes to the magnetic field in localized areas of the patient to build an image. The coils making up the electromagnets expand and contract so forcefully that they produce a thudding as loud as 120 decibels—comparable to a jet engine.*

THE JOSEPHSON JUNCTION

THE MAIN CONCEPT | In 1962, Welsh graduate student Brian Josephson devised a remarkable superconducting quantum device that won him the Nobel Prize eleven years later—the Josephson junction. It consists of two small segments of superconductor with a barrier between them, which could be an insulator or a conventional electrical conductor. Part of the complex quantum effect behind superconductivity involves pairs of electrons acting as if they are a single entity as a result of an interaction with the lattice of the superconductor. These "Cooper pairs," named for US physicist Leon Cooper who discovered them, play a key role in the Josephson junction. Just as a single quantum particle can tunnel through a barrier, Josephson predicted that Cooper pairs would also do so. And he showed that when an alternating current was put across a Josephson junction, the junction would provide extremely sensitive voltage measurements depending on the frequency of the current. Josephson's paper describing the junction enabled a number of potential applications to be developed by other physicists, although Josephson himself was only really interested in the underlying physics. For example, Josephson junctions have found their way into experimental quantum computers, and in astronomy are used to produce very wide-spectrum equivalents of the charge-coupled devices used in digital cameras.

DRILL-DOWN | The SQUID, or "superconducting quantum interference device," is the application of a Josephson junction with the widest potential use. SQUIDs employ Josephson junctions to detect tiny changes in the nearby magnetic field, producing changes in the voltage across the junctions. SQUIDs are being tried out in everything from quantum computers and variants of the MRI scanner to unexploded bomb detectors. Here, a SQUID-based detector is used to map out tiny variations in the Earth's magnetic field due to the intervening objects. The sensitivity of the SQUID means it can map out objects with unrivaled clarity. It's also better than any alternatives at a distance and works through undergrowth or water.

PROBABILITY REIGNS
Page 54

TUNNELING
Page 76

SUPERCONDUCTORS
Page 128

MATTER | *Josephson's paper on the Josephson junction is extremely detailed, displaying an intensity of character in the physicist—just twenty-two at the time. One of his lecturers, Philip Anderson, remarked that teaching Josephson "was a disconcerting experience for a lecturer . . . because everything had to be right or he would come up and explain it to me after class."*

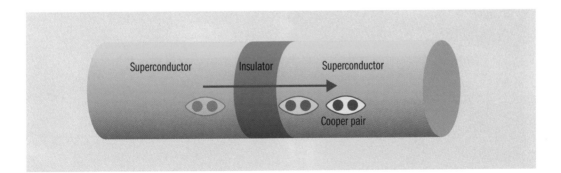

Superconductor   Insulator   Superconductor

Cooper pair

QUANTUM DOTS

THE MAIN CONCEPT | For many applications of quantum technology, it can be useful to pin down a quantum particle. Depending on the particle, different types of trap have been employed to keep a particle in place. For example, photons have been held in mirrored cavities, and charged particles can be held using electromagnetic forces to repel their charge from all directions. This is fine for a laboratory experiment, but too bulky to be incorporated into a commercial electronic device. A quantum dot is an extremely small semiconductor device capable of trapping an electron. As a result, it can act as an artificial atom. When an electron takes a quantum leap from a higher to a lower shell in an atom, the energy difference is given off as a photon—the atom has produced light. A quantum dot can behave similarly. The electron held in the dot is given extra energy, then drops back, emitting a photon. When a crystal composed of many quantum dots has an electrical current put across it, it produces light with a color that depends on the dot's size and shape, generating striking colors. Quantum dots can also be used as single-electron transistors. Here, the quantum dot acts like a miniature flash memory, capable of holding data without power.

DRILL-DOWN | Flash memory, used in memory sticks and SSD computer memory, stores data without the need for a constant electrical current. In flash memory, each bit of storage is an isolated conductor surrounded by insulator. This conductor is charged up to represent a 1 or discharged to represent a 0—because of the insulation, interaction with it can be performed only by quantum tunneling. In a quantum-dot single-electron transistor, that conductor (known as an island) is home to a single electron, rather than the multiple-electron charge in flash memory. This makes the quantum dot a good candidate for a qubit, the fundamental unit of storage in a quantum computer.

MATTER | *Perhaps the most dramatic example of an electromagnetic trap for a quantum particle was demonstrated in 1980 by Hans Dehmelt of the University of Washington. He isolated a single barium ion (a charged atom). When illuminated by the right color of laser light, that ion was visible to the naked eye as a pinprick of brilliance floating in space.*

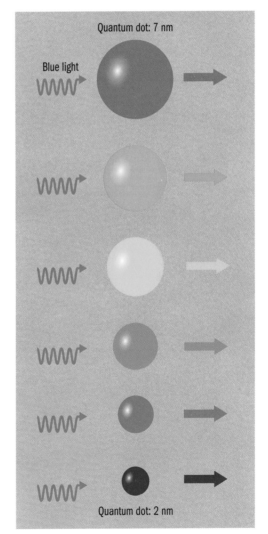

Quantum dot: 7 nm

Blue light

Quantum dot: 2 nm

QUANTUM OPTICS

THE MAIN CONCEPT | In a sense, all optical devices are quantum—they handle photons, and quantum electrodynamics (QED) describes the way that they work. So, for example, reflection off a mirror or the focusing action of a lens are quantum phenomena. However, just as electronics has been transformed by our understanding of quantum physics, so the apparently impossible can be undertaken optically using technology constructed to make explicit use of quantum phenomena—the field of quantum optics, also called photonics. One option is to use metamaterials. These are specially constructed lattices, or patterns of holes in metal sheets, that have the remarkable property of a negative refractive index. When light passes through a metamaterial, it bends the opposite way to when passing into or out of glass. Optical lenses hit a resolution limit around the wavelength of light, but this negative refractive index enables a metamaterial device to bring optical focus down to a scale previously available only to electron microscopes. Another photonic technology is a photonic crystal. Unlike metamaterials, photonic crystals exist in nature—for example producing the iridescence in an opal, a butterfly's wing, or a peacock's tail. But artificial photonic crystals could provide the equivalent of semiconductors in electronics, enabling the production of optical computers where photons, rather than electrons, do the work.

DRILL-DOWN | The most remarkable application of quantum optics is more reminiscent of *Harry Potter* or *Star Trek* than traditional physics. Some metamaterials can make an object invisible by bending light around the object to make it disappear. This has been done on a small scale with microwaves, but is harder to produce with visible light, as the materials used absorb too much of the light to work effectively. However, there are alternative mechanisms that either optically amplify the restricted output of the metamaterial or use a photonic crystal to control the way that the light is diffracted—so we may still have a form of invisibility cloaking from quantum technology.

MATTER | *Quantum optical devices are now ubiquitous in the form of LEDs (light-emitting diodes). These bulbs, which generate light by a quantum effect where electrons plunge into "holes" in semiconductors, giving off photons, have been around since the 1950s. However, the recent addition of blue LEDs to red and green, enabling white light output, has seen a transformation of low-energy lighting.*

THE QUANTUM ATOM
Page 28

QUANTUM ELECTRODYNAMICS
Page 66

WINDOWS & BEAM SPLITTERS
Page 74

SUPERFLUIDS

THE MAIN CONCEPT | Around the same time Heike Kamerlingh Onnes discovered superconductivity, he also noticed an oddity in the behavior of the liquid helium he was using to cool his superconducting mercury. At around -455.8°F (-271°C), the helium suddenly underwent a dramatic increase in its ability to conduct heat. What was happening was a mystery, and little else was made of it until 1938 when Pyotr Kapitsa, working in Russia, and John Allen and Don Misener in the UK, established that the helium was undergoing as remarkable a transition as does a superconductor when it cools. At this critical temperature, liquid helium suddenly lost all viscosity, becoming what would be later known as a superfluid. Viscosity is a measure of the "gloopiness" of a substance— the more viscous it is, the more it resists flowing. Just as superconductors lose all electrical resistance at their critical temperature, so superfluid helium loses all resistance to movement when cooled sufficiently. Once a superfluid is set in motion, unless it reaches the critical temperature, it will never stop flowing. Superfluidity is the rare example of a quantum phenomenon that is directly visible to the human eye—stir superfluid helium and you can see its continuous rotation, while superfluids in vessels attempt to escape from any orifice.

COLLAPSING WAVE FUNCTIONS
Page 56

SUPERCONDUCTORS
Page 128

BOSE–EINSTEIN CONDENSATES
Page 140

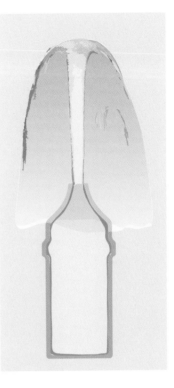

DRILL-DOWN | Helium in the form of a superfluid creeps up the walls of a container as a thin film, and if the container is not sealed, it will continue over the rim and flow out. Suitably shaped vessels can also produce a self-powering superfluid fountain. This behavior has provided the first practical use of a superfluid, in the 1983 Infrared Astronomical Satellite. The mirror of an infrared telescope needs to be kept at a constant low temperature to avoid distortion of the image. A container of superfluid helium was used, shaped so that a tiny amount pumped itself out at a time, in the process maintaining the temperature of the satellite.

MATTER | *The helium atoms in a superfluid form a special type of medium known as a Bose–Einstein condensate, where the atoms share a single quantum wave function. This applies only to the most common helium variant, helium-4. However, surprisingly, helium-3 can also become a superfluid at -459.67°F (-273.15°C) when its atoms pair up, rather like the Cooper pairs that enable superconductivity.*

BOSE–EINSTEIN CONDENSATES

THE MAIN CONCEPT | Most of us were taught at school that matter has a total of three states: solid, liquid, and gas. With the development of Crookes tubes and other early electronic devices, a fourth state of matter was discovered, which would later be called a plasma. This is like a gas, but instead of being composed of atoms, is made up of ions, which are electrically charged atoms that have either gained or lost electrons. However, quantum physics has introduced a fifth state, the Bose–Einstein condensate. A Bose–Einstein condensate is a supercooled gas of bosons (particles such as photons). Because of the low temperatures required to form the condensate, most of the quantum particles are at the lowest energy state, and they begin to behave as if they are a single collective particle, sharing a wave function. The result is a material where large collections of particles undergo processes normally associated with single particles. So, for instance, the quantum double-slit experiment can be run using condensates. This is also why a superfluid behaves as a single entity. As yet, Bose–Einstein condensates have not found a practical use. However, it has been suggested that a Bose–Einstein condensate could be used in a detector for stealth aircraft, monitoring tiny changes in gravitational pull.

Bose-Einstein condensate | Solid | Liquid | Gas | Plasma

Low   Temperature   High

DRILL-DOWN | The basic particles making up matter and light come in two forms—bosons and fermions. Bosons, which include photons, can have many identical particles crammed together, all in the same state. Fermions, such as electrons or protons, obey the Pauli exclusion principle, allowing only one particle at the same location in the same state. Fermions have quantum spin of $\frac{1}{2}$, whereas bosons have whole integer spin. This means that compound particles such as atoms can be either bosons or fermions depending on their makeup. So, for example, helium-4 is a boson, but helium-3 is a fermion. This is why helium-3 needs to pair up to form a superfluid.

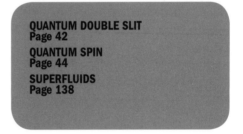

QUANTUM DOUBLE SLIT
Page 42

QUANTUM SPIN
Page 44

SUPERFLUIDS
Page 138

MATTER | *The most dramatic demonstration using a Bose–Einstein condensate was at Harvard, when Danish physicist Lene Hau used one to capture light. A laser was shone into a condensate, creating a pathway through the opaque material for a second laser. When the first laser was switched off, the light from the second was trapped in a mix of matter and light called a dark state.*

QUANTUM CHROMODYNAMICS

THE MAIN CONCEPT | With quantum electrodynamics (QED), Richard Feynman and the other developers of the theory found a way to cover interactions between matter and light, explaining electromagnetism and the way that photons carry the electromagnetic force. However, there was not an equivalent for the strong nuclear force, which is responsible for attraction between the quarks that make up protons and neutrons, and for holding together the atomic nucleus. Unlike an electron, quarks have two charges—the familiar electrical charge and the "color" charge, which comes in three different types: "red," "blue," and "green" (there is no actual color involved here—it's just a name). Just as QED describes electromagnetic interactions, in the 1970s, an equivalent approach was developed to describe strong nuclear force interactions, called quantum chromodynamics, or QCD. Where the photon carries the electromagnetic force, bosons known as gluons carry the strong nuclear force. Unlike photons, the gluons can interact with each other and have a color charge. This makes QCD messier than QED, with more complex Feynman diagrams, and means the forces that are produced by QCD work very differently. This is why we don't see "naked" quarks. The forces between quarks get stronger as the particles are separated, meaning that the quarks always stay inside particles such as protons.

DRILL-DOWN | The "color" scheme used in quantum chromodynamics is arbitrary, in the sense that the particles aren't really colored—but it was chosen for a reason. Just as the primary colors of red, blue, and green combine to make white, quarks always combine so that their colors produce "white." Where three quarks combine to make a proton or neutron, there must be one each of red, blue, and green. Similarly, in particles called mesons, which are made up of just two quarks, there must always be a combination of, a red quark and an anti-red quark, so the result is a cancellation of the colors back to pristine white.

ANTIMATTER
Page 64

QUANTUM ELECTRODYNAMICS
Page 66

FEYNMAN DIAGRAMS
Page 70

MATTER | *It might seem that the devisors of QCD chose the wrong colors, because most of us are taught that the primary colors are red, yellow, and blue. However, these aren't the true primaries. Red, green, and blue are the primaries. Pigments, which absorb some colors, take their opposites, magenta, yellow, and cyan—simplified for children to red, yellow, and blue.*

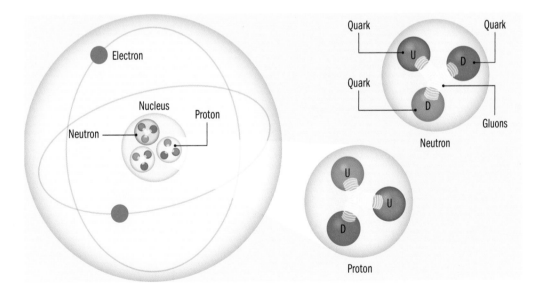

QUANTUM BIOLOGY

THE MAIN CONCEPT | For a long time, it was thought that the warm, wet conditions in biological organisms made it impossible for explicit quantum biological mechanisms to exist. However, more recently, it has been discovered that a number of biological processes depend on quantum physics. One of the earliest discoveries dates back to the 1970s and involves enzymes. We're familiar with enzymes helping biological washing powders digest stains. Primarily, though, enzymes are biological catalysts making processes inside organisms, such as the digestion of food, go faster. This catalysis often involves making it easier for protons or electrons to get across a barrier, enabling a chemical reaction to take place. Some of these particles would have enough energy to get past the barrier anyway, but enzymes make it easier for other particles to use quantum tunneling to get through. The result is reactions that are significantly speeded up, in some cases making them thousands of times faster. As well as this increased speed, quantum effects of the catalyst make a sufficiently large difference that, without them, many living organisms, including humans, would not be able to function. It is expected that a wide range of other quantum processes, including photosynthesis and tunneling across DNA base pairs, causing mutations, will be verified.

DRILL-DOWN | Deoxyribonucleic acid, (DNA), is the complex molecule that provides the "blueprint" for life. A primary mechanism of evolution is due to errors introduced when DNA is duplicated, errors that may have a quantum cause. DNA is shaped like a spiral staircase. When it divides to duplicate, the "treads" of the staircase, called base pairs, split down the middle. Each half of a base pair ends in a proton—which is capable of tunneling across to the opposite side of the pair, changing the chemical makeup of the two halves, modifying the genetic code. As a result, the data stored in the DNA could be altered, producing a new variant, or mutation.

MATTER | *It's thought that quantum processes could act as a natural quantum computer in plant photosynthesis. The energy produced in photosynthesis has to be passed to a different part of the plant's cell, with a number of options for routing. Somehow, the best route is selected, perhaps via a wave-like process using a probabilistic quantum mechanism that tries all possible routes.*

WAVE/PARTICLE DUALITY
Page 30

PROBABILITY REIGNS
Page 54

TUNNELING
Page 76

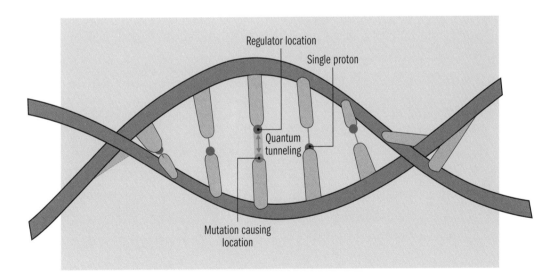

Regulator location

Single proton

Quantum tunneling

Mutation causing location

QUANTUM GRAVITY

THE MAIN CONCEPT | Between them, quantum
theory and relativity support the bulk of modern physics.
However, there is a problem—the two are incompatible.
Albert Einstein's general theory of relativity is "classical"—
in it, the force of gravity is continuously variable. And
quantum theory assumes space-time is not capable of
warping. It might seem that there isn't much need to
make a unification. Quantum theory is extremely effective
at describing small objects, while general relativity kicks
in for large-scale subjects, which are the only ones where
the weak force of gravity is significant. However, there
are some applications where the two aspects are forced
together. For example, big bang theory covers the entire
universe, but begins with a near-dimensionless point,
where quantum physics should reign supreme. Similarly,
although the concept of a black hole emerged from the
general theory of relativity (in fact, from the very first
solution of the equations, made soon after the theory
was published) it seems that the heart of a black hole
should also be a near-dimensionless point, requiring
quantum physics to explain its behavior. Some believe
such a unification is possible with concepts such as string
theory or loop quantum gravity—others think we will
need to totally rewrite at least one of these highly
successful theories.

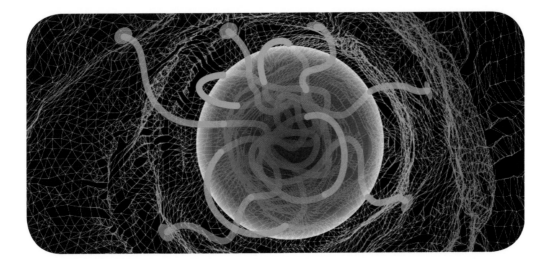

DRILL-DOWN | A number of attempts have been put forward to provide a unified approach that delivers quantum gravity. Perhaps the best known is string theory (or more properly, the overarching M-theory of which it forms a part). As a simple description, this sounds very attractive—all particles become vibrating variants on the same fundamental object, a string. However, the theory requires more spatial dimensions than we observe, and fails to make any testable predictions. Another alternative theory, loop quantum gravity, envisages a quantum framework for space-time itself, but as yet is less well formulated than string theory and does not fulfill all the requirements to combine quantum physics and general relativity.

MATTER | *If gravity were quantized, we would expect that, like the existing quantum forces such as electromagnetism and the strong nuclear force, it would have a carrier particle. In the case of electromagnetism, this is the photon— for gravity, the hypothetical particle is the graviton, but gravity is so weak that detecting a graviton is not feasible with any currently envisaged technology.*

DIRAC'S EQUATION
Page 60

QUANTUM FIELD THEORY
Page 62

QUANTUM CHROMODYNAMICS
Page 142

GLOSSARY

ALGORITHM—a step-by-step set of mathematical and logic-based instructions to undertake a calculation or solve a problem. Most computer programs use algorithms.

BLACK BODY—a theoretical object that absorbs all the light energy that falls on it, and emits light with colors that are purely dependent on its temperature.

COSMIC RAYS—high-energy particles that hit the Earth's atmosphere from outer space. On impact, cosmic rays produce a whole range of extra particles, including positrons.

DETERMINISTIC—something that is theoretically entirely predictable if we have all the details about it (as opposed to being random).

DIFFRACTION—the bending of a wave (typically light) when it hits an obstacle or slit. The amount the wave bends depends on its frequency.

DIFFRACTION GRATING—a plate with a repeated pattern of thin bars or ridges that break a beam of light into its spectrum, either by passing through it or reflection, more effectively than a prism.

ELECTRODYNAMICS—the physics of moving electrical charges.

ELECTROMAGNETIC RADIATION—a phenomenon produced by the interaction of an electric and a magnetic wave. Includes radio, microwaves, infrared, visible light, ultraviolet, X-rays, and gamma rays.

ELECTRON—a fundamental matter particle with a negative electric charge, responsible for electricity and found around the periphery of atoms.

FIELD—a phenomenon that has a value throughout space that may vary with time. Examples include electrical, magnetic, and gravitational fields.

FREQUENCY—the number of times a wave goes through its cycle of oscillation, returning to the same position, in one second.

HALF-LIFE—the time in which half of the atoms of a radioactive substance will have undergone spontaneous nuclear decay.

GLUONS—fundamental particles that carry the strong nuclear force, which ties quarks together and holds protons and neutrons in the atomic nucleus.

HIDDEN VARIABLES—the idea that quantum particles have values for properties such as position and momentum at all times, but these values are not accessible.

IMAGINARY NUMBER—any multiple of i, the square root of -1. When combined with an ordinary number, makes up a complex number, for example, $3+4i$.

INTERFERENCE—a wave effect where two or more waves interact. In areas where the waves are oscillating in the same direction, interference strengthens the waves; elsewhere, it weakens them, producing an overall pattern.

ION—an electrically charged atom that has either gained or lost electrons.

LOCAL REALITY—"local" means that an occurrence at one point in space cannot influence another point in space without sending something to cause that influence. "Real" means that objects have properties at all times, even if those properties are not accessible.

MATRIX—a set of numbers set out in a rectangle of rows and columns. Matrixes (also known as matrices) undergo mathematical processes such as addition and multiplication, but when multiplying matrixes A and B, $A \times B$ is not the same as $B \times A$.

MODEL—in science, an analogy used to predict how an aspect of nature will behave. Traditionally based on the behavior of familiar objects, but now tend to be based solely on mathematics.

MOMENTUM—the mass of an object multiplied by its velocity.

NEUTRON—a particle found in the nucleus of an atom with no electrical charge, composed of three quarks.

NOBLE GAS—elements in the final column of the periodic table that have a full outer shell of electrons and rarely react: includes helium, neon, argon, krypton, xenon, and radon. Also called an inert gas.

NUCLEAR FUSION—joining together protons and neutrons to form an atomic nucleus: the power source of stars.

ORBITAL—the mathematically derived description of the locations where an electron in an atom is most likely to be found.

PARADOX—an apparently contradictory statement that is against common sense or accepted wisdom. Unlike a fallacy, a paradox may be true.

PHOTOELECTRIC EFFECT—the release of electrons and hence the production of an electrical current when light hits a metal or semiconductor.

PHOTON—a fundamental particle that is a component of a beam of light and that is the carrier of the electromagnetic force.

POSITRON—a fundamental particle that is the antimatter equivalent of an electron: like an electron but with a positive charge. Also known as an antielectron.

PRISM—a block of transparent material that has a triangular cross section. When light hits a prism at the correct angle, it is broken into its constituent colors.

PROTON—a particle found in the nucleus of an atom with a positive electrical charge, composed of three quarks.

QUARKS—a group of six fundamental matter particles that combine in twos and threes to form other particles, notably neutrons, protons, and mesons.

RELATIVISTIC SPEEDS—speeds that are sufficiently close to the speed of light that Einstein's special theory of relativity gives a better description of their movement than Newton's laws.

SEMICONDUCTOR—a substance that is neither an electrical conductor nor an insulator, allowing the limited passage of electrical charge. Central to the development of solid-state electronics.

SHELL—structure around an atom that can be occupied by one or more electrons, with a fixed maximum of electrons in each shell.

SPACE-TIME—Einstein's relativity shows a strong link between space and time where it is no longer practical to refer to the two separately, but rather as a combined phenomenon called space-time.

SPECTRUM—the range of colors (often represented by frequencies, wavelengths, or energies) that are present in a beam of light.

SUPERPOSITION—the ability of a quantum particle to be in a state where one or more of its properties does not have a specified value, but rather two or more possibilities with different probabilities.

VACUUM ENERGY—a special case of zero-point energy: the energy present in a total vacuum due to the quantum energy fluctuations predicted by the uncertainty principle.

VIRTUAL PHOTON—a photon that is never observed but that carries the electromagnetic force when two charged particles interact.

WAVE EQUATION—an equation describing mathematically the behavior of a wave over time.

WAVE FUNCTION—a mathematical description of the state of a quantum system, typically combining a number of different properties.

WAVELENGTH—the distance in which a wave goes through a single cycle, returning to the same point in its oscillation.

FURTHER READING

BOOKS

Al-Khalili, Jim, Johnjoe McFadden. *Life on the Edge.* London: Bantam Press, 2014. Introduces the very new and fascinating field of quantum biology.

Ananthaswamy, Anil. *Through Two Doors at Once.* London: Dutton, 2018. Using the starting point of the classic "twin slits" experiment, and introducing many modern variations on the experiment that are rarely described in popular science, gives a feel for the true strangeness of quantum physics.

Baggott, Jim. *Mass.* Oxford: OUP, 2017. Digs into the apparently simple property of mass and shows how it emerges at the quantum level, also bringing in relativity.

Baggott, Jim. *Quantum Space.* Oxford: OUP, 2018. Takes the reader into the world of loop quantum gravity and the attempt to quantize space and time, through the life and work of key individuals in the field.

Ball, Phillip. *Beyond Weird.* Chicago: Chicago University Press, 2018. An exploration of the interpretations of quantum physics. Concentrates on how physicists attempt to bridge the apparent incompatibility of the behavior of familiar objects and quantum particles.

Clegg, Brian. *The God Effect.* New York: St. Martin's Press, 2006. Takes on the strangest aspect of quantum physics, entanglement, in much more detail than most popular science books.

Clegg, Brian. *The Graphene Revolution.* London: Icon Books, 2018. Explores the discovery and development of the remarkable two-dimensional material graphene – the strongest and best conducting substance known thanks to its quantum properties.

Clegg, Brian. *The Quantum Age.* London: Icon, 2014. Covers the basics of quantum theory, but focuses on the practical applications from electronics to lasers and levitating trains.

Close, Frank. *The Infinity Puzzle*. New York: Basic Books, 2013.
A detailed exploration of how physicists dealt with the problems of quantum physics producing infinite values.

Cox, Brian, Jeff Forshaw. *The Quantum Universe: everything that can happen does happen*. London: Allen Lane, 2011.
A surprisingly technical book on quantum physics from the doyen of British science TV. Not an easy read, but lots of content.

Feynman, Richard. *QED: The Strange Theory of Light and Matter*. Princeton: PUP, 2014.
Originally published in the 1980s, this transcript of a series of lectures by leading quantum physicist Richard Feynman is surprisingly approachable and still gives an excellent introduction to quantum electrodynamics.

Gleick, James. *Genius: the life and science of Richard Feynman*. London: Abacus, 1994.
Probably the best of the scientific biographies of this remarkable quantum physicist.

Gribbin, John. *Computing with Quantum Cats*. New York: Prometheus Books, 2014.
A detailed introduction to the world of quantum computing, showing how computing with qubits rather than bits could transform information technology and following the development of the latest technologies.

Gribbin, John. *In Search of Schrödinger's Cat*. New York: Bantam Books, 2011.
A classic introduction to quantum physics. Still reads well despite its age.

Hecht, Jeff. *Beam: the race to make the laser*. Oxford: OUP, 2010.
Detailed story of the development of the laser and the race between three teams to get there first.

Kakalios, James. *The Amazing Story of Quantum Mechanics*. New York: Gotham Books, 2010.
Despite the reference to comic strips, a technical exploration of quantum physics.

Pais, Abraham. *Neils Bohr's Times*. Oxford: OUP, 1991.
The definitive biography of the most enigmatic of the quantum physicists, Niels Bohr, by his close friend Pais. Insights into Bohr's physics and philosophy.

Stone, Douglas A. *Einstein and the Quantum*. Princeton: Princeton University Press, 2013.
The detail of Einstein's involvement in the development of quantum physics. For the more technically minded reader.

Susskind, Leonard, Art Friedman. *Quantum Mechanics: the theoretical minimum*. New York: Basic Books, 2014.
Closer to being an introductory textbook on quantum physics, but simplified to a degree. Requires a considerable tolerance of equations.

Wilczek, Frank. *The Lightness of Being*. New York: Basic Books, 2010.
A more in-depth look at the most popular accounts of particle physics and quantum field theory.

WEBSITES

For up-to-the-minute information on developments in quantum physics, search the following websites for "quantum":

www.newscientist.com

www.physics.org

www.physicstoday.org

www.physicsworld.com

www.quantamagazine.org

www.scientificamerican.com

INDEX

ABOUT THE AUTHOR

Brian Clegg With MAs in Natural Sciences (specializing in experimental physics) from Cambridge University and Operational Research from Lancaster University, Brian Clegg (www. brianclegg.net) worked at British Airways for 17 years before setting up his own creativity training company. He has been a full-time science writer for 15 years with over 30 titles published from *A Brief History of Infinity* (2003) to *The Quantum Age* (2015), and most recently *Professor Maxwell's Duplicitous Demon* (2019). He has also written for a range of publications from *The Wall Street Journal* to *BBC Focus* and *Playboy* magazines. He lives in Wiltshire, England.

ACKNOWLEDGMENTS

For Gillian, Rebecca, and Chelsea

With thanks to Susan Kelly, Tom Kitch, Claire Saunders, and Elizabeth Clinton for making this book a pleasure to write. A big thank you to all the great physics teachers, writers, and lecturers who have made the subject so fascinating for me over the years, particularly Richard Feynman.

Picture credits

The publisher would like to thank the following for permission to reproduce copyright material:

Alamy/ Granger Historical Picture Archive: 50 R, 51 L; Science History Images: 118 R

Getty/ Bettmann: 51 R; Hulton Archive: 119 L

Library of Congress/ Bain News Service: 16 R; Orren Jack Turner: 50 L

Science Photo Library/ Corbin O'Grady Studio: 85 L

Wikimedia 16 L, 17 R, 118 L; Karol Langner: 84 L; Nobel foundation: 17 L; Royal Society Uploader: 85 R; University of California, Irvine: 84 R; Cavendish Labratory: 119 R

All reasonable efforts have been made to trace copyright holders and to obtain their permission for the use of copyright material. The publisher apologizes for any errors or omissions in the list above and will gratefully incorporate any corrections in future reprints if notified.